MANAGING
Costs &
Resources

workbook

NVQ LEVEL 4
ACCOUNTING

Janet Brammer

OSBORNE

Published by Osborne Books Limited
Unit 1B Everoak Estate
Bromyard Road
Worcester WR2 5HP
Tel 01905 748071
Email books@osbornebooks.co.uk
Website www.osbornebooks.co.uk

Cover and page design by Hedgehog

Printed by the Bath Press, Bath

British Library Cataloguing in Publication Data
A catalogue record for this book is available from the British Library

ISBN 1 872962 49 1

CONTENTS

How to use this book

NVQ competences

1 chapter activities

2 assignments

3   central assessment tasks

ACKNOWLEDGEMENTS

The author wishes to thank the following for their help with the editing and production of the book: Michael Fardon and Jon Moore. Special thanks go to Roger Petheram and Aubrey Penning for reading, checking and advising on the development of this workbook.

Thanks are due to the Association of Accounting Technicians for their generous permission for the reproduction of Central Assessment material and also to the Lead Body for Accounting for permission to reproduce extracts from the Standards of Competence for Accounting.

AUTHOR

Janet Brammer has over ten years' experience lecturing on AAT and ACCA accountancy courses at Norwich City College. She is a Certified Accountant and worked in accountancy practice for a number of years. She has also tutored for the Open University and has written a workbook *Management Information Framework* for the ACCA distance learning scheme.

HOW TO USE THIS BOOK

Managing Costs and Resources Workbook is designed to be used alongside Osborne Books' *Managing Costs and Resources Tutorial* and is ideal for student use in the classroom, at home and on distance learning courses. Both the Tutorial and the Workbook are designed for students preparing for assessment on the two core units in Management Accounting:

- Contributing to the management of costs and the enhancement of value
- Contributing to the planning and allocation of resources

Managing Costs and Resources Workbook is divided into three sections: chapter activities, assignments and Central Assessment Tasks.

chapter activities

Chapter activities are self-contained exercises which are designed to be used to supplement the activities in the tutorial text. Many of them are more extended than the exercises in the tutorial and provide useful practice for students preparing for assessments. There are activities relating to each chapter of the tutorial text.

assignments

The assignments in this section are more extended case study activities, similar to those which are used on Central Assessments. These are intended to be used as students progress through the course, to consolidate learning and to practise the application of methods and techniques. The required chapters of the tutorial text are therefore quoted at the beginning of each assignment and also on the assignment summary on page 47.

Central Assessment Tasks

Osborne Books is grateful to the AAT for their kind permission for the reproduction of the AAT Specimen Central Assessments in this section and selected tasks from other Central Assessments. The remaining tasks are based on the kinds of tasks which have been used in Central Assessments on the two management accounting units.

answers

Answers are not provided in the text. A Tutor Pack is available separately. Please telephone Osborne Books on 01905 748071 for details or refer to the AAT pages on www.osbornebooks.co.uk

NVQ COMPETENCES

Unit 8: CONTRIBUTING TO THE MANAGEMENT OF COSTS AND THE ENHANCEMENT OF VALUE

element 1

collect, analyse and disseminate information about costs

- *valid, relevant information is identified from internal and external sources*

- *trends in prices are monitored for movements and analysed on a regular basis and potential implications are identified*

- *standard costs are compared with actual costs and any variances are analysed*

- *forecasts of trends and changes in factor prices and market conditions are consistent with previous experience of factor prices and market conditions*

- *relevant staff in the organisation are consulted about the analysis of trends*

- *reports highlighting significant trends are presented to management in an appropriate form*

element 2

make recommendations to reduce costs and enhance value

- *routine cost reports are analysed, compared with other sources of information and the implications of findings are identified*

- *relevant performance indicators are monitored and the results are assessed to identify potential improvements*

- *relevant specialists are consulted to assist in the identification of ways to reduce costs and enhance value*

- *exception reports to follow up matters which require further investigation are prepared*

- *specific recommendations are made to management and are explained in a clear and appropriate form*

Unit 9: CONTRIBUTING TO THE PLANNING AND ALLOCATION OF RESOURCES

element 1

prepare forecasts of income and expenditure

- *relevant data for projecting forecasts is identified*
- *relevant individuals are given the opportunity to raise queries and to clarify forecasts*
- *forecasts are produced in a clear format with explanations of assumptions, projections and adjustments*
- *the validity of forecasts is reviewed in the light of any significant anticipated changes*

element 2

produce draft budget proposals

- *draft budget proposals are presented to management in a clear and appropriate format and on schedule*
- *draft budget proposals are consistent with organisational objectives, have taken all relevant data into account and are agreed with budget holders*
- *annual budgets are broken down into periods in accordance with anticipated seasonal trends*
- *discussions with budget holders are conducted in a manner which maintains goodwill*

element 3: monitor the performance of responsibility centres against budgets

- *budget figures are checked and reconciled on an ongoing basis*
- *actual cost and revenue data are correctly coded and allocated to responsibility centres*
- *variances are clearly identified and reported to management in routine reports*
- *significant variances are discussed with managers and assistance is given to managers to take remedial action*

Section 1
Chapter activities

*This section contains activities which are
suitable for use with the individual
chapters of 'Managing Costs & Resources
Tutorial' from Osborne Books.*

1 MANAGEMENT INFORMATION

1.1 All kinds of information, and management information in particular, must satisfy certain criteria in order to be useful.

List and explain briefly five criteria which should be satisfied by information if it is to be useful.

1.2 Delta Ltd is an engineering firm which manufactures three products, A, B and C. Product C is produced in smaller quantities for one specific customer. The following planned and budgeted information is available for the coming year:

Overheads:	£
Production set-up costs	246,000
Raw materials inwards department	66,300
Raw materials stores	99,000
Total	411,300

Product:	A	B	C
Budgeted production (units)	40,000	30,000	15,000
Batch size (units)	2,500	3,000	1,000
Direct material cost per unit	£25	£30	£16
Direct labour cost per unit	£4	£2	£1
Direct labour hours per unit	0.5	0.25	0.125
Expected number of raw materials deliveries in year	10	6	10
Expected number of materials requisitions	16	20	30

Required: giving your answers in £ correct to 2 decimal places:

(a) Calculate a single overhead absorption rate for the total overheads of £411,300 on a direct labour hour basis. (Hint: you will first need to calculate the total labour hours required for the budgeted production of the products.)

(b) Calculate the direct cost per unit and the total cost per unit of each of the products A, B and C, using absorption costing. Use your answer to (a) to calculate the absorbed overheads.

(c) In order to apply the Activity Based Costing method to Delta Ltd, a cost driver rate must be calculated for each activity using:

$$\text{Cost driver rate} = \frac{\text{Budgeted cost pool}}{\text{Total budgeted demand for cost driver}}$$

Using this method, calculate the cost driver rates to be charged for the three activities as follows:

- Production set-up costs to be charged on the basis of number of batches.
- Raw materials inwards to be charged on the basis of number of deliveries.
- Raw materials stores to be charged on the basis of number of requisitions.

(d) Using your answers to (c) and Activity Based Costing, calculate the overheads to be included in the total cost of production for each of the products A, B and C.

(e) Using your answers to (d), calculate the total cost per unit of each of the products A, B and C, using Activity Based Costing. Show the direct cost as a subtotal before adding the overheads in each case.

1.3 Abmar Ltd manufactures one product of the same name, the Abmar. The variable costs of producing 10,000 Abmars during the year ended 30 June 20-1 were:

Direct Materials	£70,000
Direct Labour	£40,000
Variable Production Overheads	£30,000

The fixed costs incurred by Abmar Ltd in the year ended 30 June 20-1 were:

Fixed production overheads	£50,000
Other fixed overheads	£60,000

The selling price was £30 per Abmar.

Of the 10,000 Abmars produced, only 8,000 were sold during the year.

The opening stock of finished Abmars was zero and there was no opening or closing work-in-progress.

Required:

(a) Calculate the cost of one Abmar using Marginal Costing.

(b) Set out a marginal costing statement for Abmar Ltd for the year ended 30 June 20-1, showing the contribution (in total) and the total reported profit.

(c) Given that Fixed Production Overheads are to be absorbed on a per unit basis, but Other Fixed Overheads are not absorbed, calculate the absorption cost of one Abmar.

(d) Set out an absorption costing statement for Abmar Ltd for the year ended 30 June 20-1, showing the total reported profit.

(e) Calculate the difference in reported profit between your answer in (b) and your answer in (d). What is the reason for this difference?

1.4 A moving average trend in Sales Volume has been calculated as follows:

Time period:	3	4	5	6	7	8
Moving average trend (000s units)	931.0	942.4	953.3	964.6	975.7	987.0

Required:

(a) Calculate the average change in the trend per period.

(b) Forecast the trend in sales volume for each of the time periods 9, 10, 11 and 12, assuming the trend continues.

1.5 (a) Calculate a *three-point* moving average trend for the data:

> 902   890   940   900   905   950

(b) Calculate a *five-point* moving average trend for the data:

> 74   77   70   75   80   79   82   74   85   90

1.6 Spring Ltd sells a range of outdoor clothing, including lightweight showerproof jackets, for which the quarterly sales volumes over a period of three years are shown below.

	Quarter 1	Quarter 2	Quarter 3	Quarter 4
20-0	2,530	2,700	2,610	2,480
20-1	2,730	2,940	2,850	2,620
20-2	2,950	3,100	3,050	2,820

Required:

(a) Set out the Spring Ltd data in a column and calculate centred four-point moving average sales volumes for the showerproof jackets. (Use 1 decimal place in workings.)

(b) Using your answer to (a), calculate average *percentage* seasonal variations (to the nearest whole number) in the sales of Spring Ltd's showerproof jackets.

(c) Assuming that the trend and the pattern of percentage seasonal variations will continue, forecast the sales volume of Spring Ltd's showerproof jackets for each of the four quarters of 20-3.

1.7 An assistant management accountant in Snap Ltd is testing computer software for the analysis of trends and seasonal variations. After inputting several years' historical sales data relating to Snap Ltd's photographic film, the following output has been obtained:

Analysis of sales of photographic film (sales volume in numbers of films)

Regression line trend: $y = 8,000x + 150,000$

This may be written: Trend value = (8,000 x Quarter Number) + 150,000

	Seasonal Variations	
Quarter of the year	Absolute	Percentage
First	–100,000	–30%
Second	+50,000	+15%
Third	+170,000	+60%
Fourth	–120,000	–45%

Actual numbers of films sold in quarters 17 to 20 are shown below. Quarter 17 was a 'first' quarter of a year, quarter 18 a 'second' quarter, and so on.

Quarter	Number of films sold
17	185,000
18	345,500
19	471,600
20	189,000

Required:

(a) Using the regression line formula, calculate the trend for the sales of films in quarters 17, 18, 19 and 20.

(b) Using your answer to (a) and the absolute seasonal variations, calculate the resulting forecasts for the film sales in quarters 17 to 20 inclusive.

(c) Using your answer to (a) and the percentage seasonal variations, calculate the resulting forecasts for the film sales in quarters 17 to 20 inclusive.

(d) By comparing the two sets of forecasts with the actual film sales given for quarters 17 to 20, identify which method of calculating the seasonal variations gives the best estimates of actual sales of films.

(e) Using the method which you have identified as best in (d), calculate the forecast sales numbers of films for Snap Ltd for Quarters 21 to 24 inclusive.

1.8 **Required:** answer the following questions using index numbers:

(a) In the base year of a suitable price index (ie when the index number was 100), product P cost £3. The price index is now 130. What would the cost of product P be in today's terms?

(b) The market value of a house at the present time is £180,000. A suitable index for house prices is now at a level of 145. What would the price of this house be in terms of the prices 5 years ago, when this house price index was 116?

(c) A group of workers has been awarded a 2% wage increase for the next year. If the retail prices index goes up from 124 to 128 for the next year, are the workers better or worse off in real terms?

(d) Average salaries for staff in the head office of a company over 5 years are given below, together with an index of general prices for the same years.

Year	Average Salary	Price Index
1	£16,000	120
2	£16,300	122
3	£16,700	123
4	£17,000	126
5	£17,200	128

• Calculate the average salaries for each of the five years in terms of Year 5 prices. Give your answers to the nearest £.

• Comment on the results of your calculations.

2 STANDARD COSTING – DIRECT COSTS

2.1   State whether each of the following statements is true or false.

(a)   Normal amounts of wastage of direct materials are allowed for when the standard cost of a product is set.

(b)   If more product units are produced than planned, the direct materials usage variance will be adverse.

(c)   If the direct labour (total) variance is adverse, it means that the labour force worked more slowly than the standard.

(d)   Direct materials usage variances are based on the standard prices of the materials.

(e)   If forecasts under-estimate the rate of inflation when standards are set, all the direct cost variances will be adverse.

(f)   Purchasing a substitute for the normal direct material can affect both the price and usage variances.

2.2   The standard cost per unit of a product includes:

Direct material: 2.5 kg at £9.00 per kg

Direct Labour: 20 minutes at £6.00 per hour.

In a given period, the actual results were as follows:

7,620 product units were manufactured.

Direct material cost £8.80 per kg and 20,000 kg were used.

Direct labour rate was £6.60 per hour and the total cost was £16,500.

Required:

(a)   Calculate the direct material price and usage variances for the given period.

(b)   Calculate the direct labour rate and efficiency variances for the given period.

(c)   Set out a reconciliation of the standard direct cost of the actual output with the total actual direct cost, showing the variances calculated in (a) and (b).

2.3   Varan Ltd has the following budgeted and actual direct cost and production data for its single product for the last three months.

	Budget	Budget	Actual	Actual
Production units	12,000		12,300	
Direct materials	36,000 m	£223,200	37,000 m	£250,000
Direct labour	24,000 hrs	£115,200	25,000 hrs	£122,500
Total direct costs		£338,400		£372,500

Required: Calculate all the direct cost variances for Varan Ltd for the last three month period and use them to reconcile the standard direct cost for the actual production level with the actual costs.

2.4 Margan Ltd uses marginal costing and has the following budgeted and actual variable cost and production data for the month of November.

	Budget	Budget	Actual	Actual
Production units	8,500		8,200	
Variable materials	10,625 kg	£63,750	10,100 kg	£63,630
Variable labour:				
Grade I	4,250 hrs	£35,700	4,000 hrs	£34,000
Grade II	6,375 hrs	£51,000	6,300 hrs	£50,400
Total variable costs		£150,450		£148,030

Required: Calculate all the relevant variable cost variances (keeping Grade I and II labour separate) and use them to reconcile the standard marginal cost for the actual production level with the actual marginal cost.

2.5 Rust Ltd manufactures a single product, the Rek. The standard direct costs of one Rek are as follows:

Direct Material: 4 kg @ £0.80 per kg =	£3.20
Direct Labour: 1.5 hours @ £8.00 per hour =	£12.00
Total direct cost	£15.20

In October 20-1, Rust Ltd produced 9,000 Reks, and the total actual direct costs of production were £30,000 for direct material and £105,000 for direct labour.

The direct material usage variance for October 20-1 has been calculated as £800 Favourable, and the Direct Labour Efficiency Variance as £4,000 Adverse.

Required:

(a) Calculate the total standard direct cost of production for 9,000 Reks.

(b) Calculate the total actual cost of production for October 20-1.

(c) Calculate the direct material (total) variance for October 20-1 and hence calculate the direct material price variance.

(d) Calculate the direct labour (total) variance for October 20-1 and hence calculate the direct labour rate variance.

(e) Prepare a direct cost reconciliation statement for Rust Ltd for October 20-1, showing the total standard and actual costs and all the variances.

(f) Eight possible separate causes of variances are given below. For each one, state whether it appears to be a valid reason for the variances shown in (e), and if so, to which variances it may have contributed.

    1   Production was interrupted due to a machine breakdown.

    2   The supplier has improved the specification of the material.

    3   An employee's mistake caused materials to be wasted.

    4   There was a national wage increase, applicable to Rust Ltd's employees, which came into force on 1 October 20-1.

    5   The direct workers included a considerable number of trainees, who started work this month.

    6   A bonus was offered to direct workers to encourage greater efficiency.

    7   The purchasing department ordered the material from a different supplier.

    8   The employees were deliberately working slowly in October to highlight their claim for a pay increase.

3 STANDARD COSTING – FIXED OVERHEADS

3.1 Margan Ltd uses marginal costing and has the following budgeted and actual fixed cost data for the month of November.

	Budget	Actual
Production units	8,500	8,200
Fixed costs	£90,100	£85,000

Required:

(a) Calculate the fixed cost (expenditure) variance for Margan Ltd for November.

(b) Explain briefly why there is no further analysis of fixed cost variances when marginal costing is being used.

3.2 The standard direct labour time per unit of a product is 20 minutes. Fixed overheads are to be absorbed on direct labour hours at an overhead absorption rate of £12.60 per hour, based on budgeted production of 7,800 units.

In a given period, the actual results were as follows:

7,620 product units were manufactured.

Direct labour hours used were 2,500 hours.

Actual fixed production overhead amounted to £33,000.

Required:

(a) Calculate the following fixed overhead variances for this product for the given period:
- total fixed overhead variance
- fixed overhead expenditure variance
- fixed overhead capacity variance
- fixed overhead efficiency variance
- fixed overhead volume variance

(b) Which of the following statements is true for this case?

1 Production output was more than planned, resulting in a favourable efficiency variance.

2 Direct labour hours were less than planned, resulting in an adverse capacity variance.

3 Fixed overheads were over-absorbed.

4 Output was produced using less hours than the standard for the actual number of units.

5 Spending on fixed overheads was less than expected.

3.3   Varan Ltd has the following budgeted and actual direct cost and production data for its single product for the last three months.

	Budget	Budget	Actual	Actual
Production units	12,000		12,300	
Direct materials	36,000 m	£223,200	37,000 m	£250,000
Direct labour	24,000 hrs	£115,200	25,000 hrs	£122,500
Fixed production overhead		£14,400		£16,000
Machine hours	18,000 hrs		18,500 hrs	

Required:

(a)   Calculate the fixed production overhead absorption rate for Varan Ltd, based on machine hours.

(b)   Calculate the budgeted amount of fixed production overhead per unit of the product, using your answer to (a).

(c)   Calculate all the direct cost variances for Varan Ltd for the last three month period. (You may have already calculated these in Activity 2.3.)

(d)   Calculate all the fixed overhead variances for Varan Ltd for the last three month period.

(e)   Prepare a reconciliation statement for Varan Ltd's actual output for the last three months, showing the total standard and actual costs and all the variances calculated in (c) and (d) above.

(f)   Seven possible separate causes of variances are given below. For each one, state whether it appears to be a valid reason for the variances shown in (e), and if so, to which variances it may have contributed.

1   A customer increased his order for the product at short notice.

2   Due to extra demand for the product, insufficient direct materials were in stock, and a slightly different substitute material had to be obtained at short notice from a different supplier.

3   Production was interrupted due to a machine breakdown.

4   There was a national wage increase, applicable to Varan Ltd's employees, which came into force during this period.

5   A number of production staff were off sick and therefore additional overtime was worked by others.

6   A bonus was offered to direct workers to encourage greater efficiency.

7   There have been improvements in production methods since the standard was set.

3.4   Image Dry Cleaners run four shops, each of which is equipped with a dry cleaning machine. Whenever possible, each machine is run with a full load, which is on average 20 items. The shops are open six days a week, and each machine can be used to dry clean a maximum of 5 loads per day, but Image's budget is set on the basis of 4 loads per machine per weekday, and 2 loads per machine on Saturdays. Image Dry Cleaners' budgeted fixed overheads are £6,160 per week and are absorbed on a machine run basis, with the standard set at an average load of 15 items per machine run.

During the week commencing 10 September 20-1, the actual fixed overheads amounted to £6,010. Results from the Image shops showed:

	Number of machine runs	Items cleaned
North shop	18	288
South shop	24	384
East shop	20	300
West shop	20	288
Total	82	1,260

Required:

(a) Identify the output of Image Dry Cleaners and how it is measured in standard form. Calculate the fixed overhead absorption rate per machine run.

(b) Calculate all the fixed overhead variances for Image Dry Cleaners for the week commencing 10 September 20-1.

(c) Write a short report to the manager of Image Dry Cleaners, summarising the subdivision of the fixed overhead variance into expenditure, volume, capacity and efficiency variances. Include brief comments on the meaning of these variances in relation to the actual results and the usefulness of the analysis.

3.5   The Village Museum is a small private museum, which is open each day except Monday, throughout the year. The costs of running the museum are all costs which relate to time periods and do not depend on the number of visitors. Visitors are charged for entry and can stay as long as they wish in the museum on that day. The fixed costs for the first six months of the current year were budgeted as £8,400 and the total number of visitors expected was 2,400.

The actual fixed costs for the first six months of the current year were £8,670 and the actual total number of visitors was 2,550.

Required:

(a) Calculate a fixed cost absorption rate for the museum, based on the number of visitors.

(b) Calculate the fixed cost variance for the first six months of the current year, and analyse it into expenditure and volume variances. State why each of these variances has arisen.

(c) Explain briefly why analysis of the volume variance into capacity and efficiency variances would not be relevant in this case.

4 STANDARD COSTING – FURTHER ANALYSIS

4.1   (a)   Explain briefly the meaning and implications of each of the following, in relation to standard costing:

- ideal standard
- attainable standard
- basic standard

Which of these is most appropriate for the purposes of variance analysis and why?

(b)   Explain briefly what is meant by the following terms in relation to variance analysis:

- control limits
- management by exception

4.2   The standard cost per litre of a material is £3.20, based on its expected average price over the coming year. Time series analysis of the cost of this item over the last 5 years indicates that the following additive seasonal variations in the price can be expected.

Quarter 1	January to March	−£0.10
2	April to June	+£0.05
3	July to September	+£0.10
4	October to December	−£0.05

Required:

Using the given data for each of the following months, calculate the Material Price Variance for this material, and analyse it into the part expected to be due to the seasonality of the price and the part due to other influences.

(a)   In January, 18,000 litres were used, at a total cost of £54,000.

(b)   In May, 18,000 litres were used, at a total cost of £58,140.

4.3   The standard cost per metre of a material is £20, based on its expected average price over the coming year. Time series analysis of the cost of this item over the last 5 years indicates that the following proportional (multiplicative) seasonal variations in the price can be expected.

Quarter 1	January to March	+15%
2	April to June	+5%
3	July to September	−20%
4	October to December	zero

Required:

Using the given data for each of the following months, calculate the Material Price Variance for this material, and analyse it into the part expected to be due to the seasonality of the price and the part due to other influences.

(a)   In May, 6,400 metres were used, at a total cost of £124,800.

(b)   In September, 7,000 metres were used, at a total cost of £105,000.

4.4   A business set its standard price for a certain material when the appropriate price index was 148. The assumption was made that the index would rise to 150 by the time the standard was in use, and therefore the standard decided upon was £60 per unit of material, to take this into account. By the time the standard was in use, the index had actually risen to 152 and in a given month 5,800 units of material actually cost £350,900.

Required:

Calculate the Material Price Variance for this material, and analyse it into the part due to the actual change in the price index and the part due to other factors.

4.5   When standards were being decided upon, the appropriate wage rate index was expected to rise from 180 to 189, and the standard wage rate was set as £7.35 per hour to take account of this. In fact, by the time the standard was in use, an increase of 4% had been brought in for the relevant employees. In a given period, £79,056 was paid for a total of 10,800 hours.

Required:

Calculate the Labour Rate Variance for this period, and analyse it into the part due to the actual pay award and the part due to other factors.

4.6   A company imports a direct material from Beta Island and pays in Beta Dollars (B$). The standard price per unit of the material was set in B$, equivalent to £36, when the exchange rate was B$5 to the £. The exchange rate is subject to fluctuations, however, due to instability in the Beta Island economy.

Required:

For each of the following months, calculate the Material Price Variance, and analyse it into the part due to exchange rate changes and the part due to other factors.

(a)   In June the exchange rate was B$4.50 = £1. In June 7,500 units of material cost £307,500 in total.

(b)   In September the exchange rate was B$6 = £1. In September 8,000 units of material cost £256,000 in total.

4.7   A company imports a direct material from Gamma Island and pays in Gamma Dollars (G$). The standard price per unit of the material was set in G$, equivalent to £40, when the exchange rate was G$30 to the £. The exchange rate is subject to fluctuations, however, due to instability in the Gamma Island economy.

Required:

For each of the following months, calculate the Material Price Variance, and analyse it into the part due to exchange rate changes and the part due to other factors.

(a)   In July the exchange rate was G$32 = £1. In July 4,800 units of material cost £168,000 in total.

(b)   In November the exchange rate was G$25 = £1. In November 5,200 units of material cost £260,000 in total.

5 MEASURING QUALITY

5.1 The managers of a large department store wish to review the quality of the *service* (not the products) provided to customers in the various store departments. They have decided to carry out a survey, by asking customers to complete a short questionnaire.

Required:

(a) Suggest four aspects of the service that should be covered by the questionnaire.

(b) For each of the four categories listed below, give an example of a cost of quality of the service offered by the department store.

- Prevention costs

- Appraisal costs

- Internal failure costs

- External failure costs

5.2 (a) Explain briefly the implications and the benefits of implementing a policy of Total Quality Management in an organisation.

(b) Suggest how an organisation with a policy of Total Quality Management may tackle the following problems:

- A large number of complaints from customers that they are unable to get through on the telephone when they wish to place an order.

- Several cases of materials being wasted due to machine failure.

5.3 Smith's Wheels make wheels for model trains. The wheels are made by automatic machining and then assembled in pairs on axles. The wheels are sold to individual model-makers, model railway clubs, shops and to toy manufacturers to incorporate in their model trains. Accurate machining and assembly of the wheels and axles is essential for the trains to work.

After the machining process 2% of the wheels are scrapped because they are faulty. It is estimated that, after assembly, 4% of the finished products are substandard and Smith's inspection identifies three-quarters of these, which are also scrapped.

Smith's Wheels guarantee to replace any faulty wheels returned by customers.

The variable cost of making each wheel is £0.20 and the cost of the axle and assembly for each pair is £0.15, so that the variable cost of the finished product is £0.55.

In a given period, Smith's Wheels commence production with machining 40,000 wheels. Assume that all finished production which passes inspection is sold, and all faulty wheels sold are returned.

Required: for the given period:

(a)   Calculate the number of wheels scrapped after machining.

(b)   Calculate the number of substandard assembled pairs of wheels, and the quantity of these which are scrapped. How many substandard products are therefore sold?

(c)   Calculate the costs of quality associated with your answers to (a) and (b) above.

(d)   Identify two further costs of quality for Smith's Wheels which are not included in your calculations.

5.4   White Ltd runs a linen supply service for a number of hotels in a large city. Clean towels, sheets etc, supplied from White Ltd's own stock, are delivered to each hotel on a daily basis. Used linen is collected and laundered in White Ltd's own laundry.

Problems arise with the hotels if delivery is delayed, if the standard of cleanliness or the condition of items is unsatisfactory, or if the numbers of items supplied is incorrect. There have recently been a number of complaints from hotel managers about the service offered by White Ltd.

The managing director of White Ltd held a meeting with staff representatives from all departments, whose comments included the following:

•   The laundry has recently started using cheaper washing liquid.

•   The delivery vans have broken down three times in three months.

•   The requirements from the hotels come in by telephone. The calls are often made by a junior employee at the hotel and may contain mistakes. A junior White Ltd employee may take the calls.

•   Delivery routes have not been reviewed for over a year, during which time several new hotels have been added and some new road traffic schemes have been introduced in the city.

•   Some of the equipment in the laundry is out-dated and inefficient,

•   Packing staff do not have sufficient time to inspect the items thoroughly or to double check the count of items in the bags.

Required: for White Ltd's linen supply service:

(a)   Identify the features of the service which represent its value to the customer.

(b)   Suggest ways in which the problems identified at the meeting may be addressed, and the associated effects on costs of quality which would arise in each case.

5.5   Pix Ltd manufactures cameras, and has recently carried out an investigation into the reliability of one of its relatively new products, a digital camera. Investigations show that 1 in every 1,500 of these cameras quickly develops a fault and ceases to work. It is estimated that 80% of these are returned to Pix Ltd. A repair which costs the company £30 corrects the fault.

A further 2 in every 1,500 of these cameras are returned to Pix Ltd because they are considered by customers to produce unsatisfactory results. Pix Ltd gives these customers full refunds, and after checking the cameras at a cost of £10, sells them as 'reconditioned' at a discount of £100 on the usual selling price.

It is estimated that the costs of advertising in order to replace customers who were dissatisfied with

Pix Ltd's digital cameras amount to £60,000 per year. Average sales of these digital cameras are currently 75,000 per year, but Pix Ltd's managers had anticipated significant sales growth in the coming year.

Required:

List the explicit costs of quality in this case, stating the category of each and the amount where possible.

Identify an example of an implicit cost of quality in this case.

5.6   (a)   From your own point of view as a consumer, suggest the features which give a camera its value.

   (b)   From the point of view of a camera manufacturer, list four questions which may be asked in carrying out a value analysis of their products.

5.7   **Required:**

   (a)   Give two reasons why it is important to plan long-term cost reduction policies, rather than introduce crash programmes for cutting costs.

   (b)   Suggest two ways in which work study may help to reduce costs in a factory.

   (c)   List three ways in which a manufacturing company may reduce costs, other than on production.

   (d)   'Value engineering' may be applied to a new product being developed. What are the main implications this would have for the design of the product?

   (e)   Explain briefly what is meant by the statement 'variety reduction can reduce costs and enhance value'.

6 MEASURING PERFORMANCE

6.1 (a) What are performance indicators used for?

(b) Why are comparisons more useful than individual figures?

(c) List three kinds of comparisons which are useful.

6.2 The following profit and loss accounts relate to a wholesale trader selling electrical accessories such as cables, switches and so on:

M. Lomas: Profit and Loss Account for the year ended:

	30 June 20-1		30 June 20-0	
	£000s	£000s	£000s	£000s
Sales		780		675
Less: Cost of Sales				
Opening stock	60		90	
Purchases	520		410	
Less: Closing Stock	(40)	540	(60)	440
Gross Profit		240		235
Less: Expenses:				
Administration	60		45	
Selling	40	100	30	75
Net Profit		140		160

Required:

Calculate the following ratios for M. Lomas for the given years (correct to 1 decimal place):

- gross profit percentage
- net profit percentage
- each expense as a percentage of sales

Comment briefly on the original figures and on the percentages calculated.

6.3 The following are extracts from the financial accounts of Robins Ltd, manufacturers of artificial Christmas trees.

Robins Ltd: Extract from Profit and Loss Account
for the year ended 30 September:

	20-1	20-0
	£000s	£000s
Turnover	2,000	1,920
Operating Profit	267	240

Balance Sheet extract as at 30 September:

	£000s	20-1 £000s	20-0 £000s	£000s
Fixed assets (Net Book Value)		900		840
Current Assets:	120		110	
Current liabilities	(130)	(10)	(90)	20
Net Assets		890		860
Long-term loans		(50)		–
		840		860

Required:

(a)   State the formulae for the following ratios and calculate them for Robins Ltd for the given years, (correct to 2 decimal places):

- return on capital employed
- asset turnover
- operating profit margin

(b)   What is the relationship between the three ratios in (a)?

(c)   Referring to the relationship between the ratios, identify the reason for the change in the ROCE from the first to second year.

6.4   Laito Dairies Ltd is a chain of dairies (which process, bottle and distribute milk products) of which Newtown Dairy is one local division. The information below relates to Newtown Dairy.

Newtown Dairy: report for the year ended 31 July 20-1

Summary Profit and Loss Account for the year ended 31 July 20-1

	£000s	£000s
Turnover		1,300
Less: Cost of Sales		
Opening Stock	2	
Cost of Production	540	
Less: Closing Stock	(4)	538
Gross Profit		762
Administration	250	
Selling and Distribution	360	610
Operating Profit		152

Balance Sheet extract as at 31 July 20-1:

	£000s	£000s	£000s
Fixed assets	Land and Buildings	Plant	Total
At cost	800	1,200	2,000
Additions	–	300	300
	800	1,500	2,300
Accumulated depreciation	–	600	600
	800	900	1,700
Current Assets:			
Raw materials stock	3		
Finished goods stock	4		
Debtors	45		
Cash at bank	25		
	77		
Current liabilities	(110)		(33)
Net Assets			1,667

Required (working correct to 1 decimal place):

(a)   Calculate the following ratios for Newtown Dairy for the given year:

- gross profit margin
- operating profit margin
- return on capital employed (ROCE)
- asset turnover
- the average age of debtors
- the average age of finished goods stock (using average stock)

(b)   Stating the formulae you are using, calculate the current and quick (acid test) ratios for Newtown Dairy and identify one feature of the business which has an effect on these ratios in this case.

(c)   The directors of Laito Dairies Ltd consider that ROCE and Asset Turnover are important performance measures, and Newtown Dairy has failed to meet the company targets, which are:

Target ROCE: 15%   Target Asset turnover: 1.2 times

Assuming that the given balance sheet data is unchanged, calculate:

(i)   the amount of Operating Profit which Newtown Dairy would have obtained in the given year if it had achieved the company target level of ROCE

(ii)   the amount of Turnover which Newtown Dairy would have obtained if it had achieved the company target level of Asset Turnover

6.5   Walkers Ltd operates a chain of retail shoe shops. Walkers Ltd uses common accounting policies in all branches. The method of straight-line depreciation is used for fixed assets, which are mainly fixtures and fittings. The shops are rented, rent being included in 'other costs' below.

Branch managers are responsible for the control of stock and debtors and payments to creditors, but cash received is all paid into the Walkers Ltd bank account the same day.

Financial data relating to the Redridge Branch of Walkers Ltd is shown below.

Walkers Ltd Redridge Branch Year ended 31 March 20-1

Operating Statement for the year ended 31 March 20-1

	£000s	£000s
Turnover		540.0
Less: Cost of Sales		
Opening Stock	70.0	
Purchases	270.0	
Less Closing Stock	(59.2)	280.8
Gross Profit		259.2
Wages and salaries	135.0	
Depreciation	22.0	
Other costs	45.5	202.5
Operating profit		56.7

Operating net assets as at 31 March 20-1

	£000s	£000s
Fixed Assets at cost		220.0
Accumulated depreciation		88.0
Net Book Value		132.0
Working capital:		
Stock	59.2	
Debtors	27.0	
Creditors	(45.0)	41.2
Net assets		173.2

Required:

(a)   For Walkers Ltd Redridge Branch, for the given year, calculate:

- return on capital employed

- gross profit margin as a percentage

- asset turnover

- operating profit margin as a percentage

- the average age of debtors in days

- the average age of creditors in days

- the average age of stock (using closing stock) in days

(b)   The directors of Walkers Ltd have set certain targets which they consider the branches should be able to achieve. These targets are:

ROCE	37.5%
Asset Turnover	3.5 times per year
Average age of debtors	15 days
Average age of creditors	65 days
Average age of closing stock	70 days

(i)   If Redridge Branch had achieved the company target level of Asset Turnover, while maintaining prices and the existing capital employed, what percentage would the ROCE have been?

(ii)   If Redridge Branch had achieved the company targets for the average age of debtors, average age of creditors and average age of closing stock, while maintaining the same turnover and profit, what would the ROCE and the Asset Turnover have been?

(c)   Comment briefly on the results for the Redridge Branch for the given year and its performance in relation to the Walkers Ltd targets. State two limitations of the use of ratios in this way for Walkers Ltd to measure the performance of its branch managers.

7 MEASURING PERFORMANCE – FURTHER ASPECTS

7.1 Turnover and Net Profit figures are given for Ray Ltd for the five years ended 31 December 20-5 to 20-9. A suitable index for Ray Ltd's industry is also given.

	20-5	20-6	20-7	20-8	20-9
Turnover (£000s)	358	362	365	366	373
Net Profit (£000s)	55	57	59	60	62
Industry Index	131	134	136	137	140

Required: Calculate Ray Ltd's Turnover and Profit in terms of year 20-9 values. After adjusting the net profit and turnover to year 20-9 terms, calculate the net profit percentage, using the adjusted figures. Comment on the results obtained.

7.2 The following information is given for Ray Ltd for the year ended 31 December 20-9.

Turnover	£373,000
Number of employees	20
Cost of materials used	£80,000
Total cost of bought-in services	£120,000

Required: calculate the total value added and the value added per employee for the year ended 31 December 20-9 for Ray Ltd.

7.3 The following information is given for VAC Ltd for the year ended 31 August 20-1.

Turnover	£590,000
Output (product units)	40,000
Number of employees	35
Cost of materials used	£130,000
Total cost of bought-in services	£195,000
Total cost of inputs	£325,000

Required: calculate for VAC Ltd for the year ended 31 August 20-1:

- total value added
- value added per employee
- material cost per unit
- total cost of inputs per unit

7.4 For each of the following activities or aspects of work, suggest a suitable *non-financial indicator* which could be used to measure performance.

Activity or aspect to be measured

- Quality of installation service for kitchen units
- Output of carpets
- Customer satisfaction with a hotel
- Theatre ticket telephone booking service
- Website mail order books
- In-house accountancy training

7.5 Mann Ltd and Sett Ltd are two companies owned by Bow plc. Mann Ltd and Sett Ltd are similar companies using the same accounting policies. Both companies manufacture the same product, which is sold at the same price, to the house-building industry.

Financial and other information is given below for Mann Ltd, followed by certain performance indicators which have been calculated for Sett Ltd, for the year ended 31 March 20-1.

Mann Ltd Income Statement: year to 31 March 20-1

Units produced	15,000
Number of employees	12
	£000s
Turnover	1,750
Material and bought-in services	810
Production labour	210
Other production expenses	350
Depreciation – buildings	26
Depreciation – plant and machinery	90
Administration and other expenses	68
Operating profit	196

Mann Ltd: Extract from Balance Sheet as at 31 March 20-1

	£000s	£000s	£000s
Fixed assets	*Cost*	*Provision for Depreciation*	*NBV*
Buildings	1,300	520	780
Plant and Machinery	900	540	360
	2,200	1,060	1,140
Net current assets			
Stock	34		
Debtors	27		
Cash	6		
Creditors	(42)		25
			1,165

Sett Ltd: Performance indicators for the year to 31 March 20-1

•	Units produced per employee (10 employees)	1,500
•	Production labour cost per unit	£12
•	Added value per employee	£95,000
•	Asset turnover	0.8 times
•	Operating profit margin	9.8%
•	Return on capital employed	7.8%
•	Operating profit per employee	£17,150
•	Units per £1,000 of NBV of Fixed Assets	7

Required:

(a)   Calculate for Mann Ltd the eight performance indicators (as listed above for Sett Ltd) for the year ended 31 March 20-1.

(b)   Explain what is meant by 'productivity' and 'efficiency' when referring to a profit-making organisation.

(c)   From the eight performance indicators used by Bow plc above, suggest two which best measure efficiency and state whether Mann Ltd or Sett Ltd is more efficient.

(d)   From the eight performance indicators used by Bow plc above, suggest two which best measure productivity and state whether Mann Ltd or Sett Ltd has higher productivity.

(e)   Explain briefly one reason why the indicators may show one company to be more efficient, but the other to have higher productivity.

7.6   CRS Ltd produces a single product, for which the standard direct labour time is 1.5 hours per unit. For a given period, CRS Ltd budgeted for a total of 33,600 hours. The actual results for the period showed that 22,000 units were produced and the actual total direct labour hours worked were 32,500 hours.

Required: State the formulae and calculate the Efficiency Ratio, the Capacity Ratio and the Activity Ratio for CRS Ltd for this period.

7.7   You are employed by Park Ltd, a company with several subsidiaries and you have been asked to apply the balanced scorecard to monitor the performance of the subsidiaries. The following information relates to Subsidiary Green for the year ended 31 October 20-1.

Subsidiary Green Profit and Loss Account for the year to 31 October 20-1

	£000s	£000s
Sales		5,200
Less: returns		200
Turnover		5,000
Less: Cost of Sales		
Opening Finished Stock	140	
Cost of Production	1,800	
Closing Finished Stock	(170)	1,770
Gross Profit		3,230
Administration	340	
Product Development	410	
Selling and Distribution	290	
Customer Services	360	
Training	200	1,600
Operating Profit		1,630

Results of inspection of finished goods show that 2% are found to be faulty and are scrapped.

Analysis of turnover by products:

Sales of new products	2,100
Sales of existing products	2,900
Turnover as above	5,000

Analysis of turnover by customers:

Sales to new customers	1,250
Sales to existing customers	3,750
Turnover as above	5,000

Required:

(a) Identify and calculate, from the available information, one performance indicator which you could use in monitoring the financial perspective.

(b) Explain briefly what is meant by:

- The *customer perspective*

- The *internal perspective*

- The *innovation and learning perspective*

For each of these three perspectives, identify and calculate two possible performance indicators from the information given for Subsidiary Green.

8 USING BUDGETS

8.1 List and explain briefly **three** of the main advantages of budgeting for an organisation.

8.2 Explain what is meant by the term 'key (or principal) budget factor'. What is the most common key budget factor for a manufacturing company? Suggest a possible key budget factor for a charity.

8.3 The deseasonalised data for sales volumes of product Alpha for the four quarters of Year 3 is as follows:

Quarter 1: 20,400 units
Quarter 2: 20,715 units
Quarter 3: 21,020 units
Quarter 4: 21,300 units

The average percentage seasonal variations in sales volume for Alpha have been calculated as:

Quarter	1	2	3	4
	−20%	−10%	−	+30%

Required:

Calculate the forecast sales volume of Alpha for each of the four quarters of Year 4, assuming that the year 3 trend and the average seasonal variations will continue.

8.4 The actual sales revenue for product Beta for the four quarters of Year 3 was as follows:

Quarter 1: £53,600
Quarter 2: £56,650
Quarter 3: £62,610
Quarter 4: £64,600

The average absolute (additive) seasonal variations in sales revenue for Beta have been calculated as:

Quarter	1	2	3	4
	−£5,000	−£2,500	+£3,000	+£4,500

Required:

(a) Calculate the deseasonalised trend in sales revenue for product Beta for Year 3.

(b) Calculate the forecast sales revenue for Beta for each of the four quarters of Year 4, assuming that the Year 3 trend and the average seasonal variations will continue.

(c) Explain briefly any reservations you may have about the validity of the forecasts in answer (b).

8.5   In Year 3, the direct materials used by a manufacturer of plumbing accessories included:

      Material W: at £3.20 per kg
      Material X: at £8.50 per kg

and the average wages paid included:

      Skilled production wages: £6.80 per hour
      Supervisors: £22,000 per annum.

The following index numbers are available:

	Year 3	Year 4 forecast
Plumbing accessory prices	103	102
Materials prices (type W)	128	130
Materials prices (type X)	115	119
National average wages	187	190

Required:

(a)   Calculate forecast costs for Year 4, for the materials and wages listed above.

(b)   Explain briefly any reservations you may have about the forecasts calculated in (a).

8.6   Boxco Ltd is a manufacturer of heavy-duty cardboard packing cases. Two sheets of cardboard are required to make each packing case. The following forecasts are available for January 20-2:

Forecast sales demand = 1,750 packing cases

Stocks as at:	1 January 20-2	31 January 20-2
Finished packing cases	550	500
Cardboard sheets	880	920

Required:

(a)   For Boxco Ltd for January 20-2, calculate the following:
- production budget in units (packing cases)
- materials usage budget in units (cardboard sheets)
- materials purchases budget in units (cardboard sheets)

(b)   By considering the methods you have used in part (a), enter suitable formulae in the blank cells in columns B and C of the following spreadsheet format.

	A	B	C
1	*Month*	*January*	*February*
2	Sales forecast (packing cases)	1,750	2,000
3	Opening Finished Goods Stock	550	
4	Closing Finished Goods Stock	500	540
5	Production units (packing cases)		
6	Material usage per product unit	2	
7	Material usage for month (sheets)		
8	Opening Material Stock (sheets)	880	
9	Closing Material Stock (sheets)	920	950
10	Material Purchases units (sheets)		

8.7 Sunny Ltd is a manufacturer of moulded plastic toys. The standard cost of a garden toy is as follows:

> 0.9 kg of plastic at £0.80 per kg
>
> 0.25 hours of direct labour at £6.60 per hour
>
> Fixed production overheads absorbed at £3.50 per unit
>
> (Absorption rate based on budgeted production of 7,500 toys per quarter)
>
> The selling price of this toy is £9.00.

The forecast sales volumes for this toy for the first three months of the year 20-2 are:

	January	February	March
Sales units (toys)	1,800	2,000	2,300

The stock levels as at 1 January 20-2 are planned to be:

> Finished goods stock: 200 toys
>
> Raw materials stock: 750 kg of plastic

It is planned to increase finished goods stocks by 200 toys per month and increase raw materials stocks by 100 kg per month, in anticipation of higher sales in Summer.

Required:

(a) Calculate the following for each of the first three months of 20-2 and in total for the quarter:

- The production volume budget (number of toys)
- The raw materials usage budget in kg of plastic and in £
- The raw materials purchases budget in kg of plastic and in £
- The direct labour utilisation budget in hours and in £

(b) Using your answers to (a) set out a quarterly budgeted manufacturing and trading account for the quarter ended 31 March 20-2 for this toy (ie using totals calculated in (a) for the quarter). Use absorption costing and show the adjustment to gross profit for any over or under absorption of fixed production overheads which would occur in this quarter.

PRACTICAL ASPECTS OF BUDGET PREPARATION

9

9.1 The forecast demand for a component for a given period is 7,600 units. It is known that on average 5% of the finished components are rejected on final inspection.

If finished component stock levels are to remain unchanged, calculate the required units to be produced.

9.2 The forecast demand for a product for a given period is 5,300 units. The opening finished goods stock is 800 units and the required closing stock is 300 units. It is known that 4% of the product units on average are faulty and have to be scrapped.

Calculate the total production budget in units.

9.3 The standard direct labour time for a product is 2 hours per unit. 9,750 units of the product are to be produced in a given period. A new training initiative is to be brought in during the period, which will result in 2.5% of the direct labour time being used for training.

Calculate the total direct labour hours to be budgeted for the period.

9.4 The standard direct labour time for a product is 1 hour per product unit. Required production in a given period is 2,200 units. Following a new agreement on working methods, it is expected that 110% efficiency will be achieved in this period.

Calculate the labour hours to be budgeted for the required production.

9.5 The sales demand for a product in the next six months is expected to be 13,000 units. The opening finished goods stock is expected to be 1,460 units, and it is required to have 1,000 units in stock at the end of the six month period. On average, 5% of the units produced are rejected on inspection. The standard direct labour hours are 1.5 hours per unit, but this is a relatively new product and only 90% efficiency is expected in the period.

Calculate the hours to be budgeted for direct labour for the six month period.

9.6 Party Ltd is a manufacturer of paper plates. In cutting and forming the plates, 22% of the paper material is wasted. After cutting and forming, 2% of the plates have faults and are scrapped. Each batch of 100 finished plates weighs 1 kg and consists entirely of the paper material.

For the next period of production, the opening and closing stock levels are to be as follows:

	Paper (raw material)	Plates (finished goods)
Opening stock	200 kg	20,360 plates
Closing stock	350 kg	19,000 plates

The demand for finished plates for the period is 460,000 plates.

Required:

Calculate:

- the good production required
- the total production required
- the amount of paper needed to commence production
- the amount of paper required for the total production

9.7 Green Ltd is a manufacturer of garden furniture. The forecast monthly demand for its garden chairs for the year 20-2 is as follows:

20-2 Forecast sales volume (Number of chairs):

January	3,000	July	25,000
February	8,000	August	20,000
March	15,000	September	15,000
April	20,000	October	4,000
May	20,000	November	2,000
June	25,000	December	2,000

Green Ltd's stock policy is to have 30% of the next month's demand in stock at the end of each month. The stock of chairs at 1 January 20-2 and at 31 December 20-2 is expected to be 900 chairs. The direct labour hours available per month in Green Ltd (without any overtime working) are sufficient to make 22,000 chairs.

Required:

(a) Calculate the required monthly production of chairs in line with Green Ltd's stock policy.

(b) (i) Explain how production could be rescheduled in order to avoid the necessity for overtime. State the monthly production required to do this without stock levels falling below the levels stated in the current policy.

(ii) State the closing stock of chairs at the end of each month in your revised production schedule.

(c) What further information would you require in order to decide whether it would be better for Green Ltd to reschedule production or to use direct labour overtime to complete the production according to the original budget?

(d) Suggest two other alternative courses of action open to the management of Green Ltd, which would enable them to satisfy the demand for their garden chairs.

10 APPLICATION OF BUDGETING METHODS

10.1   Incremental budgeting is used by Pastel Papers Ltd, a company which manufactures stationery products. Company administration salaries for last year amounted to £180,000. The company has expansion plans which are expected to result in £30,000 of additional administration salaries (estimated at current prices). Forecast inflation is expected to result in a 2% increase in such salaries.

What would be the Pastel Papers Ltd budget for administration salaries for the coming year, using incremental budgeting?

10.2   (a)   List and explain briefly the advantages and disadvantages of incremental budgeting.

(b)   In what circumstances are

(i) zero base budgeting

(ii) programme based budgeting

most likely to be appropriate?

10.3   Production overheads in a manufacturing company have been identified as semi-variable. They consist of fixed costs of £220,000 plus £5.10 per unit produced, for a range of levels of production from 25,000 units to 40,000 units for the period.

Required:

(a)   Calculate the total production overheads for

(i) 30,000 units of production

(ii) 36,500 units of production

(b)   Why would the same method not be appropriate for calculating the production overheads for 20,000 units or 50,000 units?

10.4   You are given the total of a semi-variable cost at four different levels of activity, as follows:

Level of activity (units)	500	780	1,000	1,200
Total cost (£)	1,875	2,141	2,350	2,540

Use the high-low method to calculate the variable cost per unit and the fixed part of this semi-variable cost.

10.5 SP-CARS plc is a manufacturer of sports cars, and one of its divisions (Seats Division) makes seats for the cars. The seats are all transferred at cost to another division of SP-CARS plc, to be fitted into the cars. The demand for seats therefore depends on the total production of cars in SP-CARS plc.

For the year to 30 September 20-1, Seats Division prepared two provisional budgets, as shown below. They have been prepared on a basis which would apply to any level of demand from 5,000 to 7,500 seats. Over this range, the first three elements of cost shown are either variable or semi-variable. 'Rent, insurance and depreciation' behaves as a step cost. It is fixed for production from 5,000 to 6,250 seats, but increases by £5,000 per year when production exceeds 6,250 seats.

Seats Division provisional budgets: 12 months to 30 September 20-1

Volume (number of Seats)	6,000	7,000
	£	£
Material	108,000	126,000
Labour	150,000	165,000
Power and Maintenance	31,600	33,200
Rent, Insurance and Depreciation	85,000	90,000
Total cost	374,600	414,200

After these budgets were prepared, it was estimated that 6,000 seats would be required, and the first budget above was set as the budget for the year.

During the year ended 30 September 20-1, SP-CARS plc actually needed 6,300 seats and a performance statement was prepared, as shown below.

Seats Division performance statement: 12 months to 30 September 20-1

	Budget	Actual	Variance
Volume (number of Seats)	6,000	6,300	
	£	£	£
Material	108,000	110,000	2,000 A
Labour	150,000	160,500	10,500 A
Power and Maintenance	31,600	28,000	3,600 F
Rent, Insurance and Depreciation	85,000	88,000	3,000 A
Total cost	374,600	386,500	11,900 A

Note: F=Favourable, A=Adverse

Required:

(a) Using the data given in the two provisional budgets, calculate the fixed and variable cost elements for Material, Labour and Power and Maintenance.

(b) On investigation of the significant adverse labour variance, it is found that an error had occurred in coding the actual costs. Maintenance costs of £2,500 had been coded to Labour. Adjust the actual results to correct this error.

Using your answers to (a), prepare an amended performance statement based on flexible budgeting. Show a flexed budget compared with the corrected actual results to give the (revised) variances.

(c) Explain briefly, with reference to the case of SP-CARS plc, why a flexible budget is preferable to a fixed budget for measuring performance.

10.6 Hillfield Ltd commenced the manufacture and sale of a single product, coded HFD, on 1 July 20-1.

The original budget for Hillfield Ltd for the 3 months to 30 September 20-1 planned for production and sales volumes to be equal, both being 1,500 HFDs.

The actual results for the period were that 1,400 HFDs were produced and only 1,100 sold. The budgeted and actual figures are given below, together with attached notes.

Hillfield Ltd: Operating results for 3 months ending 30 September 20-1

	Budget	Actual
Sales volume (HFDs)	1,500	1,100
Production volume (HFDs)	1,500	1,400
	£	£
Sales	60,000	46,200
Less: Cost of Sales:		
Direct costs:		
Materials	7,500	6,380
Labour	9,000	7,150
Overheads:		
Production overheads	13,450	10,442
Total production cost of sales	29,950	23,972
Selling overheads	16,350	15,660
Total cost of sales	46,300	39,632
Profit	13,700	6,568

Notes:

(i) Direct materials and direct labour are both variable costs.

(ii) Production overheads are semi-variable. The budget for the fixed part is £10,000 for this level of activity. The actual fixed production overhead incurred was equal to the budget.

(iii) Selling overheads are semi-variable. The budget for the fixed part is £15,000. The remainder varies in relation to sales volume. The actual fixed selling overhead was equal to the budget.

(iv) There were no stocks of work-in-progress and no opening stocks of finished goods.

(v)   To calculate the actual cost of sales in the statement above, the closing stocks were valued at actual production cost. The number of HFDs was used to apportion the actual production costs between the cost of sales and the closing stock. The composition of the production cost of sales and closing stock was therefore:

	Closing Stock	Cost of Sales	Cost of Production
Number of units (HFDs)	300	1,100	1,400
	£	£	£
Direct material	1,740	6,380	8,120
Direct labour	1,950	7,150	9,100
Production overhead	2,848	10,442	13,290
Production cost	6,538	23,972	30,510

Required:

(a)   Calculate the following:

- the budgeted selling price per HFD
- the budgeted direct material cost per HFD
- the budgeted direct labour cost per HFD
- the budgeted marginal cost of production overhead
- the actual marginal cost of production overhead
- the budgeted marginal cost of selling overhead
- the actual marginal cost of selling overhead

(b)   Prepare a flexible budget statement for the operating results of Hillfield Ltd for the 3 months to 30 September 20-1, using marginal costing format and showing the variances.

(c)   Explain briefly why the actual profit reported in the marginal costing statement for the 3 months to 30 September 20-1 for Hillfield Ltd differs from the actual profit shown in the original statement. Show how the two profit figures can be reconciled.

10.7   State whether each of the following is TRUE or FALSE.

1   Zero base budgeting encourages changes in working methods.

2   Zero base budgeting encourages the introduction of budgetary slack into budgets.

3   A cost which is a constant amount per unit is described as fixed.

4   Marginal costing uses a cost for each unit of output based purely on variable costs.

5   A control period is the length of time for which a budget is prepared, usually a year.

6   It is not worthwhile to investigate favourable variances.

7   Comparing actual results with a flexible budget gives useful feedback for control purposes.

8   Feedforward might result in a revised version of the budget.

9   Variances which exceed the control limits should be identified and reported to the manager responsible.

10   Management reports should not include any non-financial information.

11 MANAGEMENT ISSUES IN RELATION TO BUDGETING

11.1 Management Accounting information is useful to managers for:

- reporting results

- highlighting problems that need action

- assisting with decision-making.

Required:

(a) For each of the three purposes given above, give two examples of management accounting information which could be used.

(b) Explain briefly why management information is important to the senior managers of a large organisation.

(c) What is the starting point for the planning process for an organisation?

11.2 The following are short extracts from a Police Authority Budget and Performance Plan for the year 20-1/20-2.

1 the Authority's five-year Best Value programme is flexible and dynamic and is reviewed each year

2 investing in information technology and essential support services including dedicated police air support coverage

3 securing the maintenance of an efficient and effective police service throughout the county

4 making more police officers available for frontline duties

5 answer 90% of '999' calls within 10 seconds

6 minimum police strength of 1,475 officers by 31 March 20-2

7 the Constabulary delivers service to clear standards covering both cost and quality

8 attend 88% of incidents requiring immediate response in rural areas within 20 minutes

9 responding to the community's request for more visible and accessible policing, thus reducing the fear of crime

10 no more violent crimes in this year in public places than in 20-0/20-1

Required: with reference to the extracts given above:

(a) Explain the term 'best value'.

(b) For each of the given extracts, state whether it relates to:
- long-term organisational goals or objectives
- strategies for achieving objectives
- short-term aims

(c) Explain briefly, using your answer to (b) as an illustration, how the long-term goals of an organisation can be expressed in short-term detailed budgets for sections of the organisation.

(d) Identify four measures of performance which could be used in the annual review, in which the level of achievement of the stated aims is assessed.

11.3 Required:

(a) Explain what is meant by the term 'controllable cost'.

(b) Explain why it is important for performance measurement to identify whether a cost is controllable by a particular manager.

11.4 The following information relates to Astro Screens Ltd, a manufacturer of computer screens. The company's organisational goals include continuous quality improvements as well as maximisation of profits.

There are four screen production departments, (SP1 – SP4), each making a particular type of screen. Department G produces a component which is transferred to the four SP departments, where it is used in the manufacture of the screens. The components are transferred at standard production cost and are not sold to other customers. The manager of Department G is responsible for the direct cost variances relating to production of the component.

Astro Screens Ltd has contracts to supply screens to ten computer manufacturers. Due to frequent changes in product specifications, the contracts are short-term and prices are re-negotiated by the managers of the SP (screen production) departments on a regular basis. The managers of the SP departments have responsibility for ensuring that the quality and delivery dates of supplies to customers can be guaranteed. They have the authority to appoint the skilled staff needed and arrange staff overtime. They are also authorised to invest in machinery or equipment necessary to do this, up to an agreed maximum for each department.

Required:

(a) For department G of Astro Screens Ltd, state whether it can be considered as

- a cost centre
- a profit centre
- an investment centre

(b) For department G of Astro Screens Ltd, suggest one reason why the transfer of components at standard production cost may not result in goal congruence.

(c) For the SP (screen production) departments of Astro Screens Ltd, state whether each department can be considered as

- a cost centre
- a profit centre
- an investment centre

(d) For the SP departments of Astro Screens Ltd, state whether the following items can be considered as controllable by each departmental manager

- sales revenue
- cost of components transferred from department G
- direct labour cost

(e) For the SP departmental managers in Astro Screens Ltd, suggest one financial and one non-financial measure of performance.

11.5 For the year ended 31 March 20-1, the senior manager of North County Library Services introduced participative budgeting for the managers of main and branch libraries. Premises costs such as rent and rates and buildings maintenance are paid from a central budget for all the libraries in the county.

The following information relates to Eastwick (North County) Branch Library for the year ended 31 March 20-1.

	Budget	Actual	Variance
	£	£	£
Library budget allocation	100,000	100,000	–
Other income (fines, charges photocopying, sales of maps, prints, old books etc.)	6,000	5,400	600 A
	106,000	105,400	600 A
Less:			
Staff salaries	85,000	85,600	600 A
Replacement books etc	7,800	7,650	150 F
Magazine subscriptions	3,200	3,350	150 A
Cleaning	2,600	2,700	100 A
Maintenance of fixtures	900	400	500 F
Depreciation of fixtures	1,800	1,800	–
Lease of photocopier	1,900	1,900	–
Heating and Lighting	2,800	2,000	800F
	106,000	105,400	600 F
Net surplus/deficit	nil	nil	nil

Required:

(a) Explain briefly what 'participative budgeting' implies for library managers.

(b) Suggest two reasons why the favourable variances shown above may have occurred, other than as a result of better motivation due to participative budgeting.

(c) Under what circumstances is it likely to be preferable for a senior manager to impose a budget, rather than take the participative approach?

11.6 Topp plc uses divisional profits as the basis for performance related pay for its divisional managers. The company's objectives include becoming a market leader for a complete range of high quality products as well as satisfying its share-holders with good returns on their investment.

Required:

(a) List three essential features for the success of Topp plc's performance related pay scheme.

(b) Suggest how a performance related pay scheme based on profits might encourage Topp plc's divisional managers to take action which does not lead to goal congruence.

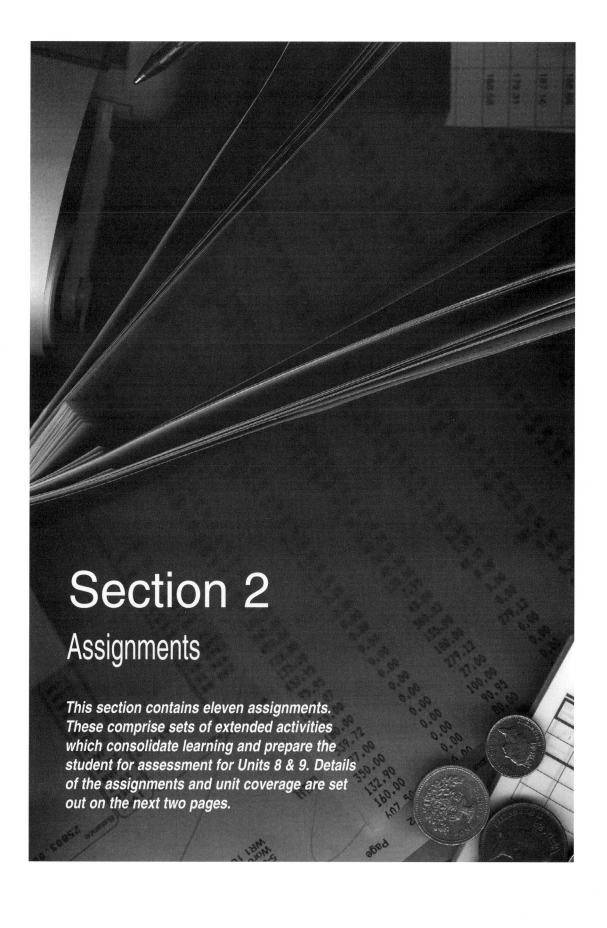

Section 2

Assignments

This section contains eleven assignments. These comprise sets of extended activities which consolidate learning and prepare the student for assessment for Units 8 & 9. Details of the assignments and unit coverage are set out on the next two pages.

INTRODUCTION TO ASSIGNMENTS

These Assignments are designed to be used for practice as you progress through the *Managing Costs & Resources Tutorial* text. It is important to be able to apply the appropriate methods and techniques that you have learned to whatever Case Study scenario you may be given.

These Assignments therefore provide a variety of situations. They are linked to specific chapters of the tutorial. The list opposite shows the relevant chapters which should be studied before attempting each Assignment.

This section is not intended to give complete coverage of both units on its own. Further practice of the application of other methods can be gained by using the activities for each chapter (Section 1) and the practice Central Assessment Tasks (Section 3).

Assignment	relevant Tutorial chapters	page
1 MEDPAK LTD Activity Based Costing	1	48
Unit 8		
2 HI-LITE Standard costing and variance analysis	1,2,3	50
3 SURE PLC Calculation and interpretation of variances	1,2,3,4	52
4 BELLA HOLIDAYS LTD CAR HIRE Variances due to exchange rate changes	1,2,3,4	56
5 COVE PLC Ratio Analysis	1,5,6	58
6 WS POTTERIES LTD Control ratios and quality management	1,5,6,7	60
Unit 9		
7 BELLA HOLIDAYS LTD ACCOMMODATION Seasonal variations and forecasting	1,8	66
8 PRIMECAST LTD Budgeting with wastage and given efficiency level	1,8,9	68
9 PLASTOYS LTD Budgeting with production scheduling	1,8,9	70
10 MOTOSTAY MOTELS LTD Budgeting in a service organisation	1,8,9,10	72
11 LUKE PLC Budgeting using marginal costing	1,8,9,10,11	74

MEDPAK LIMITED –
ACTIVITY BASED COSTING

Relevant Tutorial chapter: 1

SITUATION

Medpak Ltd is a business which packages pills into the blister packs which are issued to patients.

The pills are received in various sizes of bulk packs from the drug manufacturers. At Medpak Ltd they are then checked and coded according to the type of drug, the size of blister packs needed and other special instructions.

The machine which inserts the pills into the blister packs must be maintained in a controlled environment, and cleaned and set up for each type of drug and size of pack.

The packs are then checked, packed in boxes of 100, coded and dispatched back to the drug manufacturers for onward distribution to customers.

Just before dispatch, a sample of 1 in every 20 boxes is taken for inspection to ensure that control and quality are being maintained throughout the system.

On average, Medpak Ltd receives 2,000 boxes of pills from the manufacturers each year. These require 1,350 packaging runs on the machine, producing 180,000 blister packs. The packs are dispatched in 1,800 boxes of 100 packs.

Medpak Ltd has budgeted overheads of £382,000 per year. Activity based costing is to be introduced in order to include the cost of overheads in the cost of the work being carried out. The coding systems and automated packaging allow all necessary data to be collected on the computer system.

The assistant manager of Medpak Ltd has some accounting knowledge and codes and inputs all financial data. You are employed by a firm of accountants, AMC Services, of whom Medpak Ltd is a client.

TASKS

1   Write a memo to the assistant manager of Medpak Ltd, including the following:

   (a)   Explain briefly the main principles of activity based costing.

   (b)   Suggest the four main activities which can be identified in Medpak Ltd as described above.

   (c)   Suggest suitable cost drivers for each of the four main activities.

   (d)   Use the following examples to illustrate the allocation of overheads to cost pools:
      •   the cost of cardboard boxes for dispatch of packs
      •   the inspector's salary
      •   depreciation of the blister packaging machine
      •   delivery and insurance charges on goods sent out
      •   depreciation of bar code machine for coding drugs received

2 After all the budgeted overheads have been allocated to the four activities, the totals are as shown below. Calculate the cost driver rates to be applied to the work done for the use of each activity.

Use the information relating to budgeted levels of activity given above.

	Budgeted overheads
Receiving goods	£40,000
Blister packaging	£195,750
Dispatch	£126,000
Inspection	£20,250

3 Using activity based costing, calculate the overheads which would be included in the cost of a batch of pills which

- arrived from the manufacturer in two boxes

- required only one run on the packaging machine

- was sent back to the manufacturer in two boxes

HI-LITE – STANDARD COSTING & VARIANCE ANALYSIS

Relevant Tutorial chapters: 1,2,3

SITUATION

Hi-Lite is a provider of commercial window-cleaning services for shops and offices.

Standard costing is used in Hi-Lite for each type of service the firm provides, one of which is the cleaning of shop display windows.

The following budgeted and standard costing information relates to the shop window cleaning service.

Budgeted total fixed overheads per year	£24,000
Standard direct labour time per window	10 minutes
Planned number of windows to be cleaned per year	9,600 windows
Cost of direct materials used	£0.15 per window cleaned
Standard direct labour rate	£5.40 per hour

Fixed overheads are to be absorbed on the basis of standard direct labour hours.

It is expected that both the work done and the fixed overheads incurred will be spread evenly over the year.

The cost of direct materials per window has been calculated as the average cost of various cleaning materials used.

The actual results for Hi-Lite for the month of October 20-1 were as follows

Actual total overheads for the month	£2,250
Actual number of windows cleaned	744 windows
Actual direct labour hours worked	135 hours
Actual total cost of direct labour	£700
Actual total cost of direct materials	£125

TASKS

For Hi-Lite's shop window cleaning service:

1   Calculate the total standard cost per window cleaned.

2   Calculate the monthly budget for each element of cost (direct material, direct labour and fixed overhead).

3   For the month of October 20-1, calculate the following variances:

   (a)   Direct material total cost variance

   (b)   Direct labour rate variance

   (c)   Direct labour efficiency variance

   (d)   Fixed overhead expenditure variance

   (e)   Fixed overhead capacity variance

   (f)   Fixed overhead efficiency variance

   (g)   Fixed overhead volume variance

4   Reconcile the total standard cost of the actual work done in October 20-1 with the total actual cost, detailing all the variances calculated.

5   Explain why it is not possible in this case to split the direct material variance into price and usage variances.

6   On investigation, it is found that in October 20-1 the following factors affected the shop window cleaning service

   •   A new employee without previous experience in window-cleaning started work with Hi-Lite.

   •   A shop which was one of Hi-Lite's regular customers closed down during October.

   •   Two more shops which used Hi-Lite's service announced they would be closing in the near future.

   •   During October Hi-Lite commenced an advertising campaign to obtain new customers to replace those lost and likely to be lost through closures.

For each of these factors, state which of the variances calculated in 3 above would be likely to be affected and explain briefly whether the effect would be adverse or favourable.

SURE PLC – CALCULATION & INTERPRETATION OF VARIANCES

3

Relevant Tutorial chapters: 1,2,3,4

SITUATION

Sure plc is a manufacturer of fire-proof containers for documents, disks and other data storage media.

You are employed as a Cost Accountant by Sure plc.

The following data relate to one of Sure plc's products, a document box. Sure plc uses standard costing, and variances are calculated on a monthly basis. Variances and subvariances which exceed plus or minus 5% of budget are considered significant and are investigated.

The production of the document boxes is semi-automated and Sure plc uses absorption costing and bases the absorption of fixed overheads on machine hours.

There are two grades of labour for this product:

• Grade I employees prepare the materials and operate the machinery

• Grade II employees check and finish the products

The standard cost per unit of the document box is detailed below, together with the variance report for September 20-1 and the actual results for the month of October 20-1.

Sure plc fire-proof document box			
Standard Cost per unit			
	Quantity	Unit cost	Total
Direct material	0.5 kg	£8.20	£4.10
Direct labour Grade I	0.25 hours	£4.60	£1.15
Direct Labour Grade II	0.5 hours	£5.50	£2.75
Fixed overhead	0.6 hours*	£20.00	£12.00
Total			£20.00

* Note that fixed overhead is absorbed on machine hours, which are set at 0.6 hours per unit and the absorption rate is £20.00 per machine hour.

The fixed overhead absorption rate has been calculated on the basis of production of 1,200 boxes per month, and therefore budgeted machine hours are 720 per month and total budgeted fixed overheads are £14,400 per month.

Sure plc: fire-proof document box

Variance report September 20-1: output = 1,000 units

	£	£
Standard cost of 1,000 units		20,000
Variances		
Direct material (actual usage 485 kg)		
Price (Adverse)	97	
Usage (Favourable)	(123)	
Grade I Direct Labour		
Rate	–	
Efficiency (Favourable)	(23)	
Grade II Labour		
Rate (Adverse)	77	
Efficiency (Adverse)	275	
Fixed overheads		
Expenditure (Adverse)	200	
Capacity (Adverse)	1,600	
Efficiency (Adverse)	800	2,903
Actual cost of 1,000 units		22,903

Investigation of the significant variances has shown that there was a problem with one of the machines during September, resulting in additional maintenance being required and causing extra work on some of the units for the Grade II employees.

Sure plc: fire-proof document box

Actual results for October 20-1: 1,100 units produced

Direct material	530 kg used	cost £4,452
Grade I Direct labour	270 hours	cost £1,250
Grade II Direct labour	600 hours	cost £3,384
Machine hours used	660 hours	
Actual fixed overheads		£14,750

TASKS

1 Calculate all the variances for the fire-proof document box and prepare the variance report for October 20-1 in the same format as that given for September 20-1.

2 With reference to the information given for Sure plc, explain briefly the term 'control limits' in relation to the investigation of the causes for variances.

3 Sure plc set the standard price of the direct material when a specific price index for the material was expected to remain at 109 throughout the year 20-1. However, the index actually rose to 111 by September 20-1.

For each of the months September and October 20-1, calculate the part of the direct material price variance due to the actual change in the price index and the part due to other influences.

4 Using information from the Case Study to illustrate your answer, write a memo to the Financial Manager of Sure plc explaining why it is important to analyse trends in the monthly variances in addition to preparing the separate monthly reports.

BELLA HOLIDAYS CAR HIRE – VARIANCES DUE TO EXCHANGE RATE CHANGES

4

Relevant Tutorial chapters: 1,2,3,4

SITUATION

Bella Holidays is a UK travel agent, specialising in holidays on Ay Island, where the unit of currency is the Ay Mark (AM).

Bella Holidays sells one type of standard car hire package to its customers as an optional extra on their holiday. Bella Holidays purchases bookings for these contracts from AyCars, the owners of a fleet of hire cars on the island. Bella Holidays published the price to be charged to their customers for the car hire package throughout the season as £300, which represented a 20% mark-up on the standard cost. It was based on a standard cost of £250 or AM275, assuming that the exchange rate would average £1 = AM1.10. The exchange rate given for each month in the table below is the relevant rate for the payment of that month's invoice from AyCars. You have the following information relating to the four month period from March to June 20-1 inclusive:

20-1	March	April	May	June
Number of car hire contracts	20	18	24	21
Exchange Rate: £1 =	AM1.09	AM1.11	AM1.05	AM1.09
AyCars Invoice (AM)	5,100	4,896	6,696	6,006

TASKS

Prepare a report for your manager, Ann Miles, in the Accounts Department of Bella Holidays. The report should incorporate the three tasks shown below.

1   Set out the following information in tabulated format for the each of the four months March to June 20-1 inclusive:

(a)   the total cost in £ (to the nearest £1) to Bella Holidays of the car hire contracts, using the exchange rates given

(b)   the total standard cost for the given number of contracts, using the standard as £250 per contract

(c)   the equivalent in £ (to the nearest penny) of the standard cost, AM275, using the exchange rates given

(d)   the total standard cost in £ (to the nearest £1) for the given number of contracts, using the figures calculated in (c) above

(e)   the total price variance in £ for car hire,

(f)   the part of the price variance in £ which is due to variations in the exchange rate,

(g)   the part of the price variance in £ which is due to differences in the price charged by AyCars.

2   Assuming that you are given the average actual cost in AM per car hire contract for each of the months November 20-0 to June 20-1 inclusive, as shown in the table below, identify the underlying trend in the average actual cost, for this period, by calculating *three-point moving averages*.

Average actual cost per car hire contract:

Month	Average Actual cost Per car-hire contract (AM)
20-0	
November	240
December	245
20-1	
January	245
February	250
March	255
April	272
May	279
June	286

3   Comment on the results of your analysis in 1 and 2 above, in particular:

(a)   the usefulness of the analysis of the price variances into two parts

(b)   any identifiable trends which can be seen in the variances, without further calculations

(c)   for each of the variances calculated in Task 1 (f) and (g), an indication of the area of responsibility of the person to whom the variances should be reported and **one** suggestion as to the control action which could be taken by Bella Holidays management in relation to the variances calculated in Task 1 (g)

(d)   the usefulness of the moving average trend calculated for the average actual cost in AM for car hire contracts and your comments on this trend

COVE PLC – RATIO ANALYSIS 5

SITUATION

Cove plc is a chain of retail shops selling sports goods.

Cove plc's main competitor is Bay plc, a larger chain selling similar goods.

As a trainee management accountant in Cove plc, you are asked to analyse the published financial accounts of Bay plc and compare the performance of the two companies for the year ended 30 November 20-1.

The following data has been extracted from the financial accounts of the two companies for the year ended 30 November 20-1.

**Summary Trading and Profit and Loss Accounts
for the year ended 30 November 20-1**

	Cove plc £000s	Bay plc £000s
Turnover	18,000	22,000
Cost of sales	13,500	15,800
Gross profit	4,500	6,200
Administration	2,950	3,800
Operating Profit (Profit before interest and tax)	1,550	2,400

Summary Balance Sheets as at 30 November 20-1

	Cove plc £000s	Bay plc £000s
Fixed Assets (note 1)	3,456	4,216
Net current assets (note 2)	1,125	1,500
Total assets	4,581	5,716
Long-term loans	-	1,000
	4,581	4,716
Financed by:		
Shareholders' Funds (Capital)	4,581	4,716
	4,581	4,716

Notes:

1 Fixed assets

	Cove plc			Bay plc		
	At Cost	Accum. Deprec.	NBV	At Cost	Accum. Deprec.	NBV
	£000s	£000s	£000s	£000s	£000s	£000s
Land and Buildings	4,000	960	3,040	9,600	5,760	3,840
Fixtures and Fittings	720	408	312	620	328	292
Vehicles	240	136	104	420	336	84
Total	4,960	1,504	3,456	10,640	6,424	4,216

Straight-line depreciation is used in both companies.

2 Net current assets

	Cove plc £000s	Bay plc £000s
Stock as at 30 November 20-1	1,100	1,700
Debtors	500	680
Cash at Bank and in hand	975	320
	2,575	2,700
Current liabilities	1,450	1,200
Net current assets	1,125	1,500

Average number of employees during the year ended 30 November 20-1

Cove plc 140 employees

Bay plc 168 employees

Performance indicators

The following performance indicators have already been calculated for Cove plc for the year ended 30 November 20-1:

	Cove plc
Return on capital employed (ROCE)	33.8%
Gross Profit Margin	25.0%
Operating Profit Margin	8.6%
Asset Turnover	3.9 times
Turnover per employee	£128,571
Operating profit per employee	£11,071
Current Ratio	1.8 : 1
Acid Test Ratio	1.0 : 1
Average age of closing stock	30 days

TASKS

1   Calculate the nine performance indicators listed above for Bay plc for the year ended 30 November 20-1.

2   Write a report for the management of Cove plc, in which the following are included:

(a)   A table presenting the nine performance indicators listed above for both companies for comparison.

(b)   Your comments on the relative performance of the two companies in the year ended 30 November 20-1, referring to the original data and the performance indicators.

(c)   A brief explanation of the limitations of this analysis of the results of the two companies.

WS POTTERIES LTD – CONTROL RATIOS & QUALITY MANAGEMENT

Relevant Tutorial chapters: 1,5,6,7

SITUATION

WS Potteries Ltd is a company which manufactures pottery mugs and plates.

The mugs and plates are produced in two grades: standard and premium. The standard items are produced in large batches and are decorated by a mechanised process using transfers.

The premium items are moulded by machine in the same way as the standard items, but are decorated by hand painting and higher quality materials are used throughout. Hand painting enables WS Potteries Ltd to take orders for individually personalised items in this range, in addition to designs which are used regularly.

Direct costs are higher for the Premium range. This is due to the use of higher quality materials and the skilled labour for hand decoration. The individually personalised items in the Premium range have the highest direct costs per unit, because the hand decoration takes more time for these items.

You are employed in the accounts department of WS Potteries Ltd and have been asked to:

• analyse the following data, relating to weekly production for a period of 4 weeks,

• comment on measures of performance and suggestions for improvements

WEEK:	1	2	3	4
Total production (units)	10,916	10,700	11,250	11,200
Machine operators:				
Number of operators	10	10	10	10
Hours paid	400	400	400	400
Productive hours	368	355	375	375
Hand decorators:				
Number of decorators	3	3	4	4
Hours paid	120	120	160	170
Productive hours	105	100	140	148
Units decorated	1,008	985	1,400	1,350

Note: 'Units decorated' includes all Premium items, some of which are individually personalised to order.

You have ascertained that the Week 3 above represents exactly the standard (budgeted) levels of activity, capacity and efficiency and that all workers are paid on the basis of a 40-hour week.

The expected split of the production of 11,250 units per week between the different types of product is as follows:

	Mugs	*Plates*	*Total*
Standard Grade	8,000	1,850	9,850
Premium Grade	1,000	400	1,400
Total	9,000	2,250	11,250

These figures are based on averages, however, as special orders may alter the production scheduling in any given week.

Your investigations have revealed that a new hand decorator commenced work at WS Potteries Ltd in Week 3, and that a number of special orders for personalised Premium plates had to be completed by the end of Week 4.

You have also been told that the numbers of units produced and the numbers of units decorated, given above, represent units which have passed inspections at the end of each process. These quantities do not include units which have been broken or damaged during production or rejected as substandard. Quantities of rejects are not recorded.

WS Potteries Ltd treats the cost of packaging of the products as a direct cost. More expensive packaging materials are used for the Premium grade mugs and plates and specially printed boxes are used for the individually personalised items. The cost of packaging materials used for the units produced in the given period has been analysed as follows, to the nearest £1:

WEEK:	*1*	*2*	*3*	*4*
Total production (units)	10,916	10,700	11,250	11,200
Standard Packaging	£991	£972	£985	£985
Premium Packaging	£200	£195	£224	£275
Printed Boxes	£4	£5	£140	£150

You have investigated the costs of packaging and have found that the costs of packing material for standard items has been maintained at 10p per item, but the cost of materials for packing premium products has increased in Week 4, from 20p to 25p per item. The cost of printed boxes has also increased in Week 4, from 50p to 60p per box.

The increasing cost of packaging has given rise to a discussion between members of the management team, as to whether the same, cheaper packaging materials should be used for all items. The supervisor of the Packing Department argues that this would result in more breakages of Premium products, and that the printed box is an important part of the personalised items.

Opinions which are being put forward centre around the benefits of 'cost reduction', 'value analysis' and 'total quality management'.

TASKS

Prepare a report for the Management Accountant of WS Potteries Ltd, including the following information:

1   (a)   Units produced per machine operator in each of the 4 weeks.

(b)   The activity (production volume) ratio for the machine operators, based on Week 3 as the standard.

(c)   The efficiency ratio for machine operation for each week of the period, using Week 3 as 100%.

(d)   Units produced per Hand Decorator in each of the 4 weeks.

(e)   The efficiency ratio for hand decoration for each week of the period, using Week 3 as 100%.

(f)   Brief comments on the meaning of the activity and efficiency ratios and on the performance of the machine operators and hand decorators in the given period.

2   Include in your report brief explanations of what is meant by the terms 'cost reduction', 'value analysis' and 'total quality management', using the packaging discussion to illustrate your answer.

3   Taking into account ALL the information you have available above, make **two** recommendations in your report as to how the reporting of performance could be improved in WS Potteries Ltd and explain briefly the benefits to the company of your suggested improvements.

7

BELLA HOLIDAYS ACCOMMODATION – SEASONAL VARIATIONS & FORECASTING

Relevant Tutorial chapters: 1,8

SITUATION

Note: Assignment 4 is also based on Bella Holidays, but is completely separate. It does not have to be completed before this assignment.

Bella Holidays is a UK travel agent, specialising in holidays on Ay Island, where the unit of currency is the Ay Mark (AM).

The following information relates to the cost per week of a standard twin self-catering apartment in the main resort on Ay Island. Bella Holidays purchases bookings for these apartments from Ay Development Company, the owners of the property on the island.

It has been determined that the average cost per week of a standard twin self-catering apartment is subject to seasonal variations in the four quarters of the year as follows:

	Quarter 1	Quarter 2	Quarter 3	Quarter 4
Variation (Ay Marks)	−100	−50	+125	+25

The average actual cost per week (in Ay Marks) of the apartments has been calculated from the actual amounts charged by Ay Development Company for the last eight quarters as follows:

20-0

Quarter 4	AM 212

20-1

Quarter 1	AM 150
Quarter 2	AM 265
Quarter 3	AM 502
Quarter 4	AM 470

20-2

Quarter 1	AM 404
Quarter 2	AM 520
Quarter 3	AM 760

TASKS

Prepare a report for your manager, Ann Miles, in the Accounts Department of Bella Holidays. The report should incorporate the four tasks shown below.

1   Set out the following information in tabulated format for the period from Quarter 4 of 20-0 to Quarter 1 of 20-3 inclusive:

(a)   the average actual cost per week of a standard twin self-catering apartment in the main resort on Ay Island, for the eight quarters for which this is given,

(b)   the given seasonal variation for each quarter

(c)   the underlying trend in the average actual cost, for these eight quarters, calculated by 'deseasonalising' the data, that is removing the seasonal variations from the actual figures

(d)   forecasts for the trend for the last quarter of 20-2 and the first quarter of 20-3, using the average change in the trend per quarter

(e)   forecasts for the actual cost for the last quarter of 20-2 and the first quarter of 20-3

2   Draw a graph for the period from Quarter 4 of 20-0 to Quarter 1 of 20-3 inclusive, showing the information given in the table in 1 above.

3   Comment on the usefulness of the identification of the trend and the forecasting which you have carried out in **1** above.

4   Comment on what further information you require to improve your report for management accounting purposes and how this information would be used.

PRIMECAST LTD – BUDGETING WITH WASTAGE AND GIVEN EFFICIENCY LEVEL

8

Relevant Tutorial chapters: 1,8,9

SITUATION

Primecast Ltd is a manufacturer of cast stone-effect ornamental products for parks and large gardens.

Budgets are prepared for periods of 12 weeks, each week being 5 working days.

The budgeted direct labour rate is £6.00 per hour and the basic working week is 40 hours for full-time employees. Any additional hours are paid at an overtime rate of time and a half, ie £9.00 per hour. There are 13 full-time employees working on production.

In the next 12-week budget period, two products (codes LB1 and SB2) are to be manufactured and the following information is available for preparation of the budget.

Product	LB1	SB2
Budgeted sales units	2,200	4,500
Direct material in each completed unit	6 kg	2 kg
Direct labour hours per unit	1 hour	0.6 hour

The budgeted cost of direct material is £3.00 per kg. 10% of the material input to the production process is lost and this must be allowed for in the material usage budget.

For the next period, the target efficiency ratio for the productive hours of direct labour is 95%. After budgeting for the required production time, a further 20% of the total production time is to be added, to allow for breaks and for time spent on indirect work such as preparation and cleaning of equipment.

The budgeted opening and closing stock levels for the next 12-week period are as follows:

	Opening stock	Closing stock
Direct Material	3,700 kg	4,300 kg
Product LB1 completed units	150 units	800 units
Product SB2 completed units	825 units	600 units

(There are no stocks of work in progress).

TASKS

1   For Primecast Ltd for the next 12-week period, calculate the following:

(a)   the production budget in units of each of the two products LB1 and SB2

(b)   the total direct material usage budget in kg

(c)   the total direct material purchases budget in kg and in £

(d)   the standard direct labour hours required for production

(e)   the productive hours required at 95% efficiency

(f)   the total hours to be budgeted for production workers

(g)   the total budgeted cost of production labour including overtime premium

2   Suggest **two** possible ways in which Primecast Ltd could reduce or eliminate the necessity for overtime payments.

PLASTOYS LTD – BUDGETING WITH PRODUCTION SCHEDULING

Relevant Tutorial chapters: 1,8,9

9

SITUATION

Plastoys Ltd is a company which manufactures plastic toys. The toys are produced from different colours of plastic material by automated processes. Plastoys Ltd's sales quantities are affected by seasonal variations. As the toys are moulded by machines, production quantities are limited by the available machine hours.

You are an assistant to the management accountant in Plastoys Ltd and you have been asked to analyse the following data, relating to quarterly production for a period of 2 years, and forecast sales quantities for the following five quarters. The forecast sales can then be used to prepare a production budget for the next year.

QUARTER:	1	2	3	4
YEAR 20-0				
Total Sales (units)	13,600	20,534	41,400	62,420
YEAR 20-1				
Total Sales (units)	13,960	21,076	42,425	64,035

You have ascertained that the seasonal variations in sales quantities of Plastoys Ltd have been found to approximate to the multiplicative (proportional) model, as follows:

QUARTER:	1	2	3	4
Actual units as % of trend	40%	60%	120%	180%

You have also been told that the numbers of units produced per quarter cannot exceed 40,000 units, because of the limited availability of machine hours. It is currently the policy in Plastoys Ltd to produce sufficient units, so that the stock of toys at the end of each quarter is at least 40% of the forecast quantity of Sales for the following quarter.

TASKS

Prepare a report for the Managing Director of Plastoys Ltd, including the following information:

(a) The trend in Sales Quantities (Units), calculated by deseasonalising the actual data for each of the 8 quarters given (years 20-0 and 20-1).

(b) Forecasts of the trend in Sales Quantities for each of the 4 quarters of 20-2 and the first quarter of 20-3

(c) Forecasts of the actual Sales Quantities for each of the 4 quarters of 20-2 and the first quarter of 20-3

(d) The minimum number of units required in closing stock, according to current policy, in the last quarter of 20-1 and in each of the 4 quarters of 20-2.

(e) The draft Production Budget (in units) for the 4 quarters of 20-2, without taking into account the limitation on machine hours, but applying the policy on stock levels by using the minimum amounts required, as calculated above.

(f) An adjusted Production Budget (in units) for the 4 quarters of 20-2, taking into account the limitation on machine hours and applying the policy on stock levels. (Note that the policy states 'at least' 40%: the level of 40% may be exceeded).

(g) A brief explanation of **one** reservation you may have relating to the budget proposals calculated above for the given period.

(h) Taking into account all the information you have available above, suggest one way in which the profitability of Plastoys Ltd could be improved without increasing the machine hours available. Explain briefly the financial and the non-financial benefits to the company which would result from your proposal.

MOTOSTAY MOTELS LTD – BUDGETING IN A SERVICE ORGANISATION

10

Relevant Tutorial chapters: 1,8,9,10

SITUATION

Motostay Motels Ltd is a company which owns and runs motels situated on motorways and major routes around the UK.

All the motels have one type of room, with exactly the same standard of facilities. The accommodation is priced at £50 per room per night throughout all the motels and is not dependent on the number of people occupying the room or the time of year. The motels remain open all the year round (365 days).

Motostay Motels Ltd has a central office which houses a computerised booking and accounting system which is linked up to all the motels where the bookings are taken.

The external maintenance of the buildings is also centralised, but day-to-day repairs and internal maintenance are the responsibility of each motel manager. This work is normally sub-contracted to local businesses, on an annual service charge basis. The individual motels do not employ maintenance staff.

Cleaning staff are employed by each motel manager and are paid on an hourly basis. Administrative staff are also employed, to take bookings, work on reception, deal with guests' payments and input data to the computer system. Staff must be available for this work every day from 6 am until midnight. The manager of the motel normally covers part of this work.

The standards set by Motostay Motels Ltd for customer service are applied in all the motels. Every occupied room is thoroughly cleaned every day and all bedlinen and towels replaced, whether or not there is a change of guests. The rooms contain consumables for the tea and coffee making facilities and also for the bathrooms. For costing purposes it is assumed that these are all replaced every day in each room which is occupied. Rooms which are unoccupied are kept clean, but this takes the cleaners less time than for the occupied rooms, and the laundry and consumables costs are not incurred.

Other costs incurred include fees for TV channels, which are not dependent on whether the rooms are occupied or not, and electricity, which is reduced when the rooms are unoccupied.

You are a trainee manager with Motostay Motels Ltd and have been given the following information about a particular motel, reference number M215, which contains 80 rooms. The cost unit for cost accounting purposes is the room-night, ie one room for one night. From the information given above, it can be seen that certain costs per room-night will differ between occupied and unoccupied rooms.

During the year to 31 March 20-1, the level of occupancy at the motel was 52%. (Level of occupancy is the number of occupied room-nights as a percentage of the total available room-nights.)

During the year ended 31 March 20-1, the following unit costs have been incurred in Motel M215:

	Occupied Room-night £	Unoccupied Room-night £
Laundry	7.50	–
Cleaning (wages)	4.80	0.60
Cleaning (materials)	0.20	0.10
Consumables	3.25	–
Electricity	3.85	1.65
TV channel fees (£)	0.95	0.95

Other Fixed Costs:

Salaries (manager and administration staff)	£135,000 for the year.
Contracts for internal maintenance	£55,000 for the year.

Some changes in the above costs are anticipated for the year commencing 1 April 20-1, as follows:

Laundry charges to increase by 2%

Cleaning wages to increase by 5%

Consumables to increase by 4%

All fixed costs to increase by 5%

TASKS

As part of your training course, you are required to set out your answers to the following in the form of a report to the Management Accountant of Motostay Motels Ltd.

1 For Motel M215, for the year ended 31 March 20-1:

- Calculate the total available room-nights for the year.

- Calculate the number of occupied room-nights, given the level of occupancy as 52%.

- Calculate the corresponding number of unoccupied room-nights.

- Calculate the total costs for the motel for the year.

- Calculate the total sales revenue for the motel for the year, assuming all sales were at £50 per room per night.

- Calculate the profit for the motel for the year.

2 For Motel M215 for the year from 1 April 20-1 to 31 March 20-2, assuming the anticipated cost increases occur:

- Calculate the revised unit costs for an occupied room-night and an unoccupied room-night.

- Calculate the total costs at a level of occupancy of 60%.

- Calculate the total costs at a level of occupancy of 80%.

- Calculate the profit for the motel for the year at each of these two levels of occupancy, assuming all sales are at £50 per room per night.

- Calculate the profit for the motel for the year, if the 80% level of occupancy was achieved by introducing a special offer. This offer would mean that all extra sales above the 60% level were at half price.

3 Comment on the results of your calculations in 1 and 2 above. Also explain briefly two important considerations to be taken into account by Motostay Motels Ltd, when determining whether to introduce special offers to boost sales.

LUKE PLC – BUDGETING USING MARGINAL COSTING

11

Relevant Tutorial chapters: 1,8,9,10,11

SITUATION

You are the Management Accountant of Luke plc, a company which manufactures a single product.

The budget for Luke plc for the year ended 31 July 20-1 was originally prepared on the basis of production and sales of 40,000 product units.

The Chief Executive of Luke plc did not consider that the budgeted profit would meet company targets, and imposed a budget based on a reduction of the selling price and a higher sales volume. In order to improve the profit, there was also a requirement to increase productivity and to cut fixed administration costs.

The original and revised budgets are given below. Production labour is treated as a fixed cost and the revised budget does not allow for any increase. The additional production is to be achieved by improvements in productivity. Power is a semi-variable cost. 'Other fixed costs' include Administration Costs, which the Chief Executive expects to be reduced by £100,000 for the year.

The actual results for Luke plc for the year ended 31 July 20-1 are also given. The Chief Executive was concerned that the actual net profit was lower than that shown in the original budget.

Production reached the revised volume of 46,000 units, but sales volume was 42,000 units, therefore closing stock of finished goods was 4,000 units. (There were no opening stocks of finished goods and no opening or closing work-in-progress).

Luke plc: Budgets for the year to 31 July 20-1

	Original Budget		Revised Budget	
Production and Sales	40,000 units		46,000 units	
	£000s	£000s	£000s	£000s
Turnover		2,000.0		2,070.0
Less: Production Cost of Sales				
Direct Materials	360.0		414.0	
Production Labour	289.0		289.0	
Power	90.0	739.0	102.0	805.0
Gross Profit		1,261.0		1,265.0
Less:				
Other Fixed Costs		850.0		750.0
Net Profit		411.0		515.0

Luke plc: Actual results for the year to 31 July 20-1

	£000s	£000s
Turnover (42,000 units sold)		1,890.0
Less: Cost of Sales		
Opening Stock	–	
Production cost of 46,000 units		
Direct Materials	409.4	
Production Labour	295.6	
Power	77.0	
	782.0	
Less Closing Stock (4,000 units)	(68.0)	714.0
Gross Profit		1,176.0
Less:		
Other Fixed Costs		788.0
Net Profit		388.0

TASKS

1   Calculate, for Luke plc for the year to 31 July 20-1:

- the original budgeted selling price per product unit
- the revised budgeted selling price per product unit
- the budgeted direct material cost per product unit
- the fixed and variable parts of the budgeted cost of power
- the actual variable cost of power, given that the actual fixed part of the cost was £2,000 less than the budget

2   Using marginal costing, prepare a performance statement for Luke plc for the year to 31 July 20-1 showing

- a flexed budget for sales of 42,000 units and production of 46,000 units, based on the revised budget (Closing stock is to be valued at budgeted variable cost.)
- the actual results set out in marginal costing format, with closing stocks valued at actual variable cost
- the variances for turnover and each element of cost

3   Write a report to the Chief Executive of Luke plc

- explaining briefly the conditions under which it is likely that employees will be motivated to work towards an imposed budget

- commenting on any indications in the actual results, shown in your performance statement for the year to 31 July 20-1, as to whether the employees were motivated by the imposed budget

- stating the two main reasons why the actual profit for the year to 31 July 20-1 was less than the profit shown in the imposed revised budget

- stating the main reason why the actual profit for the year to 31 July 20-1 was less than the profit shown in the original budget

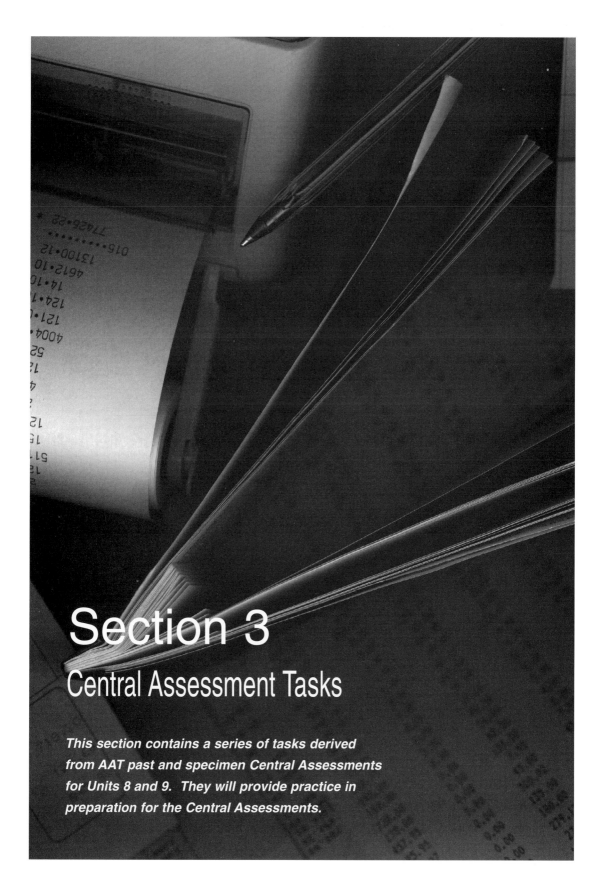

Section 3
Central Assessment Tasks

*This section contains a series of tasks derived
from AAT past and specimen Central Assessments
for Units 8 and 9. They will provide practice in
preparation for the Central Assessments.*

CENTRAL ASSESSMENT TASKS

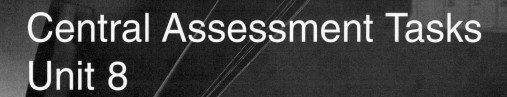

Central Assessment Tasks
Unit 8

Kings Limited and Micro Circuits Limited

recommended timing 3 hours plus 15 minutes reading time

SECTION 1: KINGS LTD

DATA

Kings Ltd manufactures several types of small machines. You are working as an assistant cost accountant in Kings Ltd and have been requested to carry out the following tasks.

Department D of Kings Ltd produces a single type of moulded and hand-finished component (code D1) for use by other departments of the company in the manufacture of its products. Kings Ltd uses standard costing in all its departments. Separate absorption rates are calculated for each department for fixed overheads, based on direct labour hours. The standard cost per unit of Component D1 includes 75g of direct material at £4.40 per kg and 30 minutes of direct labour time at £8.00 per hour. The planned direct labour hours for Department D are 15,000 per month. Kings Ltd has apportioned budgeted fixed overheads of £270,000 per month to Department D.

The actual results for Department D in the month of June 20-1 were as follows:

- Direct material purchased and used cost a total of £8,400 at £4.20 per kg.

- The actual direct labour cost was £120,400 and the hours worked were sufficient to produce 28,000 units of Component D1, although production was actually only 25,000 units.

- The total amount of fixed overhead was in line with the budgeted amount.

Note: 1 kg = 1,000g.

Task 1.1

(a)   Calculate the standard cost per unit of Component D1.

(b)   Calculate for department D of Kings Ltd for the month of June 20-1:

    (i)   the actual quantity of direct material used

    (ii)   the actual number of direct labour hours

    (iii)   the actual total amount of fixed overhead

(c)   Calculate the following variances for department D of Kings Ltd for June 20-1:

    (i)   direct material price variance

    (ii)   direct material usage variance

    (iii)   direct labour rate variance

    (iv)   direct labour efficiency variance

    (v)   fixed overhead expenditure variance

    (vi)   fixed overhead capacity variance

    (vii)   fixed overhead efficiency variance

    (viii)   fixed overhead volume variance

(d) Prepare a report for Ben Wray, the production manager for Department D, showing the following information:

    (i) the standard cost per unit of Component D1, as calculated in (a)

    (ii) a statement reconciling the total actual cost of the units of production of Component D1 in June 20-1 with the total standard cost for that number of units, showing the variances calculated in (b)

    (iii) brief comments on the statement you have prepared, referring in particular to the meaning and usefulness to Ben Wray of the calculated fixed overhead variances

DATA

On receipt of the variance report, Ben Wray, who is a relatively new member of staff at Kings Ltd, replies as follows:

KINGS LTD

MEMORANDUM

To: Assistant Cost Accountant

From: B. Wray, Production Manager, Dept. D

Date: 17 July 20-1

Subject: Variance Report for June 20-1.

I have a number of queries about the variance report for June 20-1. I have had a meeting with the Management Accountant, who is trying to improve the efficiency and usefulness of the reporting system. He suggested introducing control limits and using exception reporting. I am meeting him again next week and would like to use the June report as an example of the effects of these and also of the sort of problems I have. Could you clarify the following points for me:

1   Can variances be caused by errors, which would not necessarily be my responsibility?

2   It seems that some of these variances are outside my control, so would an alternative form of report be more useful? I really need information on which I can take action.

3   What difference would it make to the effectiveness of the reporting system if the Management Accountant's ideas of introducing control limits and using exception reporting were introduced?

4   Referring to June 20-1 specifically, would the following factors have made a difference to the variances, and if so, which ones would be affected? Can you calculate the part of the variance which is due to these factors?

    • In June, several trainees joined the department and the experienced workers had to show them the working methods.

    • Due to the slow working caused by training the new workers, we fell behind with production at one point, and I had to agree 150 hours of exceptional overtime at time and a half in order to catch up. The cost of this all went into the direct labour total for the month.

    • The training resulted in wastage of about 60 kg of the direct material, due to work having to be rejected.

Task 1.2

Prepare a reply to Ben Wray's memorandum, showing the following information and referring to your answer to Task 1.1 where appropriate.

a) reply to question 1 in the Memorandum, including in your answer two examples of errors which may cause variances

b) reply to question 2 in the Memorandum, explaining what is meant by 'controllability' of costs and suggesting how its consideration could improve the form of the report

c) reply to question 3 in the Memorandum, explaining the terms 'control limits' and 'exception reporting' and the improvements that may be made using these ideas

d) reply to question 4 in the Memorandum, including in your answer an explanation of which variances would be affected by these factors, together with calculations where possible.

SECTION TWO: MICRO CIRCUITS LTD

DATA

You are employed by Micro Circuits Ltd as a financial analyst reporting to Angela Frear, the Director of Corporate Strategy. One of your responsibilities is to monitor the performance of subsidiaries within the group. Financial and other data relating to subsidiary A is reproduced below.

Subsidiary A

Profit and Loss Account for the year to 30 November 20-8

	£000s	£000s
Sales		4,000
Less returns		100
Turnover (note 1)		3,900
Material	230	
Labour	400	
Production overheads (note 2)	300	
Cost of production	930	
Opening finished stock	50	
Closing finished stock	(140)	
Cost of Sales		840
Gross Profit		3,060
Marketing	500	
Customer support	400	
Research and Development	750	
Training	140	
Administration	295	2,085
Operating Profit		975

Extract from Balance Sheet at 30 November 20-8

	£000s	£000s	£000s
Fixed Assets	Land and	Plant and	Total
	Buildings	Machinery	
Cost	2,000	2,500	4,500
Additions	–	1,800	1,800
	2,000	4,300	6,300
Accumulated depreciation	160	1,700	1,860
	1,840	2,600	4,440
Raw material stock	15		
Finished goods stock	140		
	155		
Debtors	325		
Cash and Bank	40		
Creditors	(85)		
			435
Net assets			4,875

Notes

1   Analysis of Turnover

	£000s		£000s
Regular customers	3,120	New products	1,560
New customers	780	Existing products	2,340
	3,900		3,900

2   Production overheads include £37,200 of reworked faulty production

Task 2.1

Angela Frear asks you to calculate the following performance indicators for Subsidiary A for the year to 30 November 20-8, in preparation for a board meeting:

(a)   the return on capital employed

(b)   the asset turnover

(c)   the sales (or operating profit) margin

(d)   the average age of debtors in months

(e)   the average age of finished stock in months.

DATA

One of the issues to be discussed at the board meeting is a suggestion made by one of the directors that Micro Circuits Ltd should introduce a policy of Total Quality Management. Angela Frear is aware that some of the directors are opposed to this on the basis that it would reduce the company's profits.

Task 2.2

Angela Frear asks you to prepare briefing notes for the board meeting. Using the above data and the data from task 2.1 where necessary, your notes should

(a)   list and explain briefly the main implications of the introduction of Total Quality Management

(b)   suggest **two** items shown in the data given for subsidiary A which should be reduced if Total Quality Management were introduced and explain the reasons

(c)   identify **two** cost items in the data for Subsidiary A which would be likely to increase if Total Quality Management were introduced and explain the reasons

(d)   suggest **two** performance indicators, for which the data is already recorded, which could be used to measure quality in Micro Circuits Ltd subsidiaries. Show how the indicators would be calculated for Subsidiary A for the year to 30 November 20-8.

Central Assessment Tasks
Unit 8

Travel Holdings plc – LandAir & SeaAir

recommended timing 3 hours plus 15 minutes reading time

SECTION 1: TRAVEL HOLDINGS PLC

DATA

You are employed as a management accountant in the head office of Travel Holdings plc. Travel Holdings owns a number of transport businesses. One of them is Travel Ferries Ltd. Travel Ferries operates ferries which carry passengers and vehicles across a large river. Each year, standard costs are used to develop the budget for Travel Ferries Ltd. The latest budgeted and actual operating results are given below.

Travel Ferries Ltd

Budgeted and actual operating results for the year to 30 November 20-0

Operating data	Budget	Budget	Actual	Actual
Number of ferry crossings	6,480		5,760	
Operating hours of ferries	7,776		7,488	
Cost data		£		£
Fuel	1,244,160 litres	497,664	1,232,800 litres	567,088
Labour	93,312 hours	466,560	89,856 hours	471,744
Fixed overheads		466,560		472,440
Cost of operations		1,430,784		1,511,272

Other accounting information

- fuel and labour are variable costs
- fixed overheads are absorbed on the basis of budgeted **operating hours**.

Task 1.1

(a) Calculate the following information:

    (i)   the standard price of fuel per litre

    (ii)   the standard litres of fuel for 5,760 ferry crossings

    (iii)   the standard labour rate per hour

    (iv)   the standard labour hours for 5,760 ferry crossings

    (v)   the fixed overhead absorption rate per budgeted operating hour

    (vi)   the standard operating hours for 5,760 crossings

    (vii)   the standard fixed overhead cost absorbed by the actual 5,760 ferry crossings

(b) Using the data provided in the operating results and your answers to part (a), calculate the following variances:

  (i) the material price variance for the fuel

  (ii) the material usage variance for the fuel

  (iii) the labour rate variance

  (iv) the labour efficiency variance

  (v) the fixed overhead expenditure variance

  (vi) the fixed overhead volume variance

  (vii) the fixed overhead capacity variance

  (viii) the fixed overhead efficiency variance

(c) Prepare a statement reconciling the actual cost of operations to the standard cost of operations for the year to 30 November 20-0.

DATA

On receiving your reconciliation statement, the Chief Executive is concerned about the large number of adverse variances. She is particularly concerned about the excessive cost of fuel used during the year. A colleague informs you that:

• the actual market price of fuel per litre during the year was 20% higher than the standard price

• fuel used varies directly with the number of operating hours

• the difference between the standard and actual operating hours for the 5,760 ferry crossings arose entirely because of adverse weather conditions

Task 1.2

Write a Memo to the Chief Executive. Your memo should include the following:

(a) subdivide the material price variance into:

  (i) the part arising from the standard price being different from the actual market price of fuel, and

  (ii) the part due to other reasons.

(b)

  (i) for the actual 5,760 crossings, calculate the number of additional operating hours which were caused by the adverse weather conditions

  (ii) for the material usage variance, calculate the part of the variance arising from the additional operating hours and the part due to other reasons

  (iii) for the labour efficiency variance, calculate the part arising from the additional operating hours and the part due to other reasons.

(c) Suggest and explain briefly **one** way in which the reporting of variances in Travel Ferries Ltd could be improved.

SECTION 2: LANDAIR AND SEAAIR

DATA

LandAir and SeaAir are two small airlines operating flights to Waltonville. LandAir operates from an airport based at a town on the same island as Waltonville but SeaAir operates from an airport based on another island. In both cases, the flight to Waltonville is 150 air-miles. Each airline owns a single aircraft, an 80-seat commuter jet, and both airlines operate flights for 360 days per year.

You are employed as the management accountant at SeaAir and report to Carol Jones, SeaAir's chief executive. Recently, both airlines agreed to share each other's financial and operating data as a way of improving efficiency. The data for the year to 31 May 20-0 for both airlines is reproduced below, followed by the performance indicators for LandAir.

Operating Statement for the year ended 31 May 20-0

	LandAir		SeaAir	
	$000	*$000*	*$000*	*$000*
Revenue		51,840		29,700
Fuel & aircraft maintenance	29,160		14,580	
Take-off & landing fees at Waltonville	4,320		2,160	
Aircraft parking at Waltonville	720		2,880	
Depreciation of aircraft	500		400	
Salaries of flight crew	380		380	
Home airport costs	15,464	50,544	8,112	28,512
Net Profit		1,296		1,188

Extract from Balance Sheet at 31 May 20-0

	LandAir	SeaAir
	$000	*$000*
Fixed assets:		
Aircraft	10,000	10,000
Accumulated depreciation	2,500	4,000
Net book value	7,500	6,000
Net current assets	3,300	5,880
	10,800	11,880
Other operating data		
Number of seats on aircraft	80	80
Return flights per day	12	6
Return fare	$200	$275
Air-miles per return flight	300	300

Performance indicators for LandAir

Return on capital employed	12.00%
Asset turnover per year	4.80 times
Sales (or net profit) margin	2.50%
Actual number of return flights per year	4,320
Actual number of return passengers per year	259,200
Average seat occupancy (note 1)	75.00%
Actual number of passenger miles (note 2)	77,760,000
Cost per passenger mile	$0.65

Notes

1   Actual number of return passengers ÷ maximum possible number of return passengers on actual flights.

2   Actual number of passengers carried x number of miles flown.

Task 2.1

Carol Jones asks you to prepare the following performance indicators for SeaAir:

(a)   return on capital employed

(b)   asset turnover

(c)   sales (or net profit) margin

(d)   actual number of return flights per year

(e)   actual number of return passengers per year

(f)   average seat occupancy

(g)   actual number of passenger-miles

(h)   cost per passenger-mile.

DATA

On reviewing the performance indicators you have calculated for SeaAir and comparing them with those for LandAir, Carol Jones is concerned that SeaAir has a lower Return on Capital Employed, even though it has a higher Net Profit Margin. She reminds you that there is a link between the Return on Capital Employed, the Asset Turnover and the Net Profit Margin and asks you to prepare answers to the following questions in the next Task.

Task 2.2

(a)   State the equation which links the Return on Capital Employed, the Asset Turnover and the Net Profit Margin. Using the equation, calculate the Asset Turnover which SeaAir would require in order to achieve the same Return on Capital employed as LandAir, assuming SeaAir's Net Profit margin was as calculated in Task 2.1 (c) above.

(b)   Calculate the Revenue which SeaAir would have obtained in the year ended 31 May 20-0, if the Asset Turnover had been at the level calculated in (a) above, in this task.

(c)   Calculate the percentage increase in the number of passengers in the year ended 31 May 20-0 which would have been necessary in order to obtain the Revenue calculated in (b) above.

(d)   Assuming SeaAir had run the same number of flights, what would the average seat occupancy have been if the increase in the number of passengers calculated in (c) above had been achieved?

(e)   Suggest **one** way in which the Asset Turnover and hence the Return on Capital Employed could have been improved by SeaAir in the year ended 31 May 20-0, other than by increasing the number of passengers.

(f)   Suggest **one** way in which SeaAir could have increased its Revenue in the year ended 31 May 20-0 other than by improving the average seat occupancy on its flights.

Central Assessment Tasks
Unit 8

Barefoot Hotel Complex and Cass plc

recommended timing 3 hours plus 15 minutes reading time

SECTION 1: BAREFOOT HOTEL COMPLEX

DATA

You are the assistant management accountant at the Barefoot Hotel complex on the tropical island of St Nicolas. The hotel complex is a luxury development. All meals and entertainment are included in the price of the holidays and guests only have to pay for drinks.

The Barefoot complex aims to create a relaxing atmosphere. Because of this, meals are available throughout the day and guests can eat as many times as they wish.

The draft performance report for the hotel for the seven days ended 27 November 20-9 is shown below.

Barefoot Hotel Complex
Draft performance report for seven days ended 27 November 20-9

	Budget		Actual	
Number of guests		540		648
	$	$	$	$
Variable costs				
Meal costs (note 1)		34,020		49,896
Catering staff costs (notes 2,3)		3,780		5,280
Total variable costs		37,800		55,176
Fixed overhead costs				
Salaries of other staff	5,840		6,000	
Local taxes	4,500		4,200	
Light, heat and power	2,500		2,600	
Depreciation of buildings and equipment	5,000		4,000	
Entertainment	20,500		21,000	
Total fixed costs		38,340		37,800
Total cost of providing for guests		76,140		92,976

Notes

1 Budgeted cost of meals = number of guests x 3 meals per day x 7 days x $3 per meal

2 Budgeted cost of catering staff: each member of the catering staff is to prepare and serve 12 meals per hour and is paid $4 per hour.

   Cost = number of guests x 3 meals per day x 7 days x $4 ÷ 12

3 Actual hours worked by catering staff = 1,200 hours.

Other notes

The amount of food per meal has been kept under strict portion control. Since preparing the draft performance report, however, it has been discovered that guests have eaten, on average, four meals per day.

You report to Alice Groves, the general manager of the hotel, who feels that the draft performance report could be improved to provide her with more meaningful management information. She suggests that the budgeted and actual data given in the existing draft performance report is rearranged in the form of a standard costing report.

Task 1.1

(a) Use the budget data, the actual data and the notes to the performance report to calculate the following for the seven days ended 27 November 20-9:

    (i)   the actual number of meals served

    (ii)   the standard number of meals which should have been served for the actual number of guests

    (iii)   the actual hourly rate paid to catering staff

    (iv)   the standard hours allowed for catering staff to serve three meals per day for the actual number of guests

    (v)   the standard fixed overhead per guest

    (vi)   the total standard cost for the actual number of guests

(b) Use the data given in the task and your answers to part (a) to calculate the following variances for the seven days ended 27 November 20-9

    (i)   the material price variance for meals served

    (ii)   the material usage variance for meals served

    (iii)   the labour rate variance for catering staff

    (iv)   the labour efficiency variance for catering staff, based on a standard of 3 meals served per guest per day

    (v)   the fixed overhead expenditure variance

    (vi)   the fixed overhead volume variance on the assumption that the fixed overhead absorption rate is based on the budgeted number of guests per seven days

(c) Prepare a statement reconciling the standard cost for the actual number of guests to the actual cost for the actual number of guests for the seven days ended 27 November 20-9.

DATA

On receiving your reconciliation statement, Alice Groves asks the following questions:

- How much of the labour efficiency variance is due to guests taking, on average, four meals per day rather than the three provided for in the budget and how much is due to other reasons?

- Would it be feasible to subdivide the fixed overhead volume variance into a capacity and efficiency variance?

Task 1.2

Write a Memo in reply to Alice Groves. Your Memo should:

(a)   divide the labour efficiency variance into that part due to guests taking more meals than planned and that part due to other reasons

(b)   explain the meaning of fixed overhead capacity and efficiency variances

(c)   *briefly* discuss whether or not it is feasible to calculate the fixed overhead capacity and efficiency variances for the Barefoot Hotel Complex

SECTION 2: CASS PLC – AMOS LTD AND BOYD LTD

DATA

You are employed as an assistant management accountant by Cass plc. Amos Ltd and Boyd Ltd are two companies owned by Cass plc. Both companies manufacture the same product, which is sold at £250 per unit to the agricultural industry. Amos Ltd and Boyd Ltd operate in similar geographical areas and both companies use the same accounting policies, including straight-line depreciation.

Financial and other information is given below for Amos Ltd and Boyd Ltd, followed by certain performance indicators which have been calculated for Boyd Ltd, for the year ended 31 March 20-1.

Amos Ltd Income Statement: year to 31 March 20-1

	£000s	£000s
Units produced and sold	14,000	
Number of employees	16	
Turnover		3,500
Material and bought-in services	1,700	
Production labour	315	
Other production expenses	787	
Depreciation – buildings	24	
Depreciation – plant and machinery	100	
Administration and other expenses	154	3,080
Operating profit		420

Amos Ltd: Extract from Balance Sheet as at 31 March 20-1

	£000s	£000s	£000s
Fixed assets	Cost	*Provision for Depreciation*	NBV
Buildings	1,200	480	720
Plant and Machinery	1,000	600	400
	2,200	1,080	1,120
Net current assets			
Stock	178		
Debtors	65		
Cash	12		
Creditors	(95)		160
			1,280

Boyd Ltd Income Statement: year to 31 March 20-1

Units produced and sold	24,000	
Number of employees	25	
	£000s	£000s
Turnover		6,000
Material and bought-in services	3,100	
Production labour	485	
Other production expenses	1,200	
Depreciation – buildings	40	
Depreciation – plant and machinery	150	
Administration and other expenses	245	5,220
Operating profit		780

Boyd Ltd: Extract from Balance Sheet as at 31 March 20-1

	£000s	£000s	£000s
Fixed assets	Cost	*Provision for Depreciation*	NBV
Buildings	2,000	120	1,880
Plant and Machinery	1,500	450	1,050
	3,500	570	2,930
Net current assets			
Stock	260		
Debtors	95		
Cash	9		
Creditors	(154)		210
			3,140

Boyd Ltd: Performance indicators for the year to 31 March 20-1

- Units produced per employee 960
- Production labour cost per unit £20.21
- Added value per employee £116,000
- Asset turnover 1.9 times
- Operating profit margin 13.0%
- Return on capital employed 24.8%
- Operating profit per employee £31,200
- Units per £1,000 of NBV of Fixed Assets 8.2

Task 2.1

(a) Calculate the following performance indicators for Amos Ltd for the year ended 31 March 20-1 and set them out in a table with those of Boyd Ltd for comparison:

(i) units produced per employee

(ii) production labour cost per unit

(iii) added value per employee

(iv) asset turnover

(v) operating profit margin

(vi) return on capital employed

(vii) operating profit per employee

(viii) units produced per £1,000 of Net Book Value of *fixed assets*

(b) The Managing Director of Boyd Ltd has claimed that his company outperforms Amos Ltd as it achieves a much higher level of productivity.

Explain briefly what is meant by productivity and whether the performance indicators shown in (a) above for the two companies support this claim.

DATA

The Chief Executive of Cass plc requires a summary of the performance of Amos Ltd and Boyd Ltd for the year ended 31 March 20-1, emphasising in particular the efficiency of the two companies.

Task 2.2

Prepare a brief summary, to be attached to the comparative table of performance indicators, for submission to the Chief Executive of Cass plc. The summary should include the following:

(a) Explain your understanding of the term 'efficiency' when applied to a profit-making organisation.

(b) From the eight performance indicators used by Cass plc above, suggest **two** which could be used to measure efficiency and state whether they indicate that Amos Ltd or Boyd Ltd is more efficient.

(c) Explain briefly one reason why the indicators may show one company to be more efficient, but the other to have higher productivity.

Central Assessment Tasks Unit 8

Original Holidays Limited and Diamond Limited

reproduced by kind permission of AAT

recommended timing 2 hours plus 15 minutes reading time

NOTE TO STUDENTS

This assessment has been issued by AAT to provide guidance for students completing Central Assessments.

The Assessment is divided into two sections.

The recommended timing is as follows:

Section 1	70 minutes
Section 2	50 minutes

Note: subsequent AAT Central Assessments have allowed 3 hours plus 15 minutes reading time.

SECTION 1: ORIGINAL HOLIDAYS LIMITED

(Suggested time allocation: 70 minutes)

DATA

You are employed as an Accounting Technician by Original Holidays Limited. Original Holidays commenced business one year ago as a tour operator specialising in arranging holidays to the small island of Zed. Recent newspaper reports have stated that the cost of hotel bedrooms per night in Zed has been increasing over the last twelve months due to its government refusing to allow further hotels to be built despite increasing demand from tourists.

The managing director of Original Holidays, Jane Armstrong, is concerned that this will affect the profitability of the company's operations to the island. She asked Colin Ware, the financial accountant, to provide data showing the nightly cost of a bedroom charged to Original Holidays over the last four quarters. Colin's response is reproduced below.

Memo

To: **Jane Armstrong**   **Date:**   **5th January 1998**

From: **Colin Ware**

Subject: **Nightly cost per bedroom**

Thank you for you recent enquiry concerning the cost per night of a bedroom in Zed. I have analysed the amounts paid per quarter over the last twelve months and divided that amount by the number of bedrooms hired per night. The nightly cost per bedroom is as follows:

	Quarter 1	Quarter 2	Quarter 3	Quarter 4
Cost per night	£102.400	£137.760	£134.480	£68.921

(Note: all figures in pounds to 3 decimal places.)

On receiving the memo, Jane noticed that the cost to Original Holidays per bedroom per night had actually been falling over the last three quarters and has asked for your help in reconciling this with the newspaper reports. You obtain the following information.

- Over several years, there has been a consistent seasonal variation in the cost of bedrooms per night. According to the marketing manager, these are:

Seasonal variations	Quarter 1	Quarter 2	Quarter 3	Quarter 4
as percentage of trend	-20%	+5%	+40%	-25%

- A financial newspaper provides you with the following exchange rates between the UK pound and the Zed franc:

	Quarter 1	Quarter 2	Quarter 3	Quarter 4
	2,000 francs	2,000 francs	2,800 francs	3,000 francs

Task 1.1

(a) Using the quarterly exchange rates given, identify the actual nightly cost per bedroom in Zed francs for each quarter.

(b) Using the information provided by the marketing manager, identify the trend in costs in Zed francs for each quarter.

(c) Identify the quarterly percentage increase in the cost of a bedroom per night in Zed francs.

(d) Forecast the cost in British pounds of a bedroom per night for the first quarter of next year using the exchange rate for the fourth quarter.

DATA

On receiving your analysis of the cost per bedroom per night, Jane Armstrong expresses concern that the company's existing reporting system does not provide sufficient information to monitor operations. She shows you a copy of the operating statement for the third quarter prepared using the existing system. The statement excludes marketing, administrative and other head-office overheads and is reproduced below.

Original Holidays Operating Statement for the 3rd Quarter – 1997

	Budget	Actual
Number of holidays	6,000	7,800
	£	£
Turnover	1,800,000	2,262,000
Accommodation	840,000	1,048,944
Air transport	720,000	792,000
Operating profit	240,000	421,056

Jane has shared her concerns with Colin Ware, the financial accountant. He has suggested that a standard costing report, reconciling standard cost to actual cost, would provide more meaningful information for management. To demonstrate to Jane Armstrong the improved quality of a standard costing system of reporting, Colin asks you to re-analyse the operating statement for the third quarter. To help you, he provides you with the following information:

- The accommodation is a variable cost. Its usage variance is nil

- Air transport is a fixed cost and relates to the company's own 105-seat aircraft

- The budget provided for 80 return flights in the quarter with each flight carrying 75 tourists. This volume was used to calculate the fixed overhead absorption rate when costing individual holidays

- Due to operational difficulties, the aircraft only undertook 78 return flights, carrying a total of 7,800 passengers in quarter 3

Task 1.2

(a)   Using the budgeted data, calculate the standard absorption cost per holiday.

(b)   Using your answer to part (a), calculate the standard absorption cost of 7,800 holidays.

(c)   Calculate the following variances:
   (i)   material price variance for the accommodation
   (ii)   fixed overhead expenditure variance for the air transport
   (iii)   fixed overhead volume variance for the air transport
   (iv)   fixed overhead capacity variance for the air transport
   (v)   fixed overhead efficiency variance for the air transport

(d)   Prepare a statement reconciling the budgeted (or standard) absorption cost to the actual cost for 7,800 holidays.

(e)   Identify the single most important reason for the increase in the actual profit.

Task 1.3

Write a memo to Jane Armstrong *briefly* explaining what the following variances attempt to measure and giving **one** possible reason why each variance might have occurred:
- the fixed overhead expenditure variance
- the fixed overhead capacity variance
- the fixed overhead efficiency variance

SECTION 2: DIAMOND LIMITED

(Suggested time allocation: 50 minutes)

DATA

Diamond Ltd is a retail jeweller operating 30 branches in similar localities. Common accounting policies operate throughout all branches, including a policy of using straight-line depreciation for fixed assets.

All branches use rented premises. These are accounted for under 'other costs' in the operating statement. Fixed assets are predominantly fixtures and fittings.

Each branch is individually responsible for ordering stock, the authorising of payments to creditors and the control of debtors. Cash management, however, is managed by Diamond's head office with any cash received by a branch being paid into a head office bank account twice daily.

You are employed in the head office of Diamond Ltd as a financial analyst monitoring the performance of all 30 branches. This involves calculating performance indicators for each branch and comparing each branch's performance with company standards. Financial data relating to Branch 24 is reproduced below.

Diamond Ltd - Branch 24 - Year ended 31 December 1997					
Operating statement			**Operating net assets at year end**		
	£000	*£000*		*£000*	*£000*
Turnover		720.0	*Fixed assets*		
Opening stock	80.0		Cost		225.0
Purchases	340.0		Accumulated depreciation		(90.0)
Closing stock	(60.0)				
			Net book value		135.0
		360.0			
Gross profit		360.0	*Working capital*		
Wages and salaries	220.6		Stocks	60.0	
Depreciation	45.0		Debtors	96.0	
Other costs	36.8		Creditors	(51.0)	105.0
		302.4	Net assets		240.0
Operating profit		57.6			

Task 2.1

Prepare a statement showing the following performance indicators for Branch 24:

(a) the return on capital employed

(b) the gross profit margin as a percentage

(c) the asset turnover

(d) the sales (or net profit) margin as a percentage

(e) the average age of debtors in months

(f) the average age of creditors in months

(g) the average age of the closing stock in months

DATA

The financial director of Diamond Ltd is Charles Walden. He is concerned that Branch 24 is not performing as well as the other branches. All other branches are able to meet or exceed most of the performance standards laid down by the company.

Charles is particularly concerned that branches should achieve the standards for return on capital employed and the asset turnover. He also feels that managers should try to achieve the standards laid down for working capital management. The relevant standards are:

•	return on capital employed	40%
•	asset turnover	4 times per annum
•	average age of debtors	0.5 months
•	average age of creditors	3 months
•	average age of closing stock	1 month

Charles Walden has recently attended a course on financial modelling and scenario planning. Charles explains that scenario planning shows the likely performance of a business under different assumed circumstances. It requires an understanding of the relationship between the different elements within the financial statements and how these change as the circumstances being modelled change. As an example, he tells you that if the volume of branch turnover was to increase then the cost of sales would also increase but that all other expenses would remain the same as they are fixed costs.

He believes scenario planning would be particularly helpful to the manager of Branch 24, Angela Newton. Charles had previously discussed the performance of the branch with Angela and emphasised the importance of improving the asset turnover and maintaining control of working capital. However, Angela raised the following objections:

• turning over assets is not important, making profit should be the main objective

• Branch 24 has been in existence for two years less than all the other branches

Task 2.2

Charles Walden asks you to write a memo to Angela Newton. Your memo should:

(a) Show the return on capital employed that Branch 24 would have achieved had it been able to achieve the company's asset turnover during the year to 31 December 1997 while maintaining prices and the existing capital employed.

(b) Show the return on capital employed and the asset turnover for the year if Branch 24 had been able to achieve the company's standards for the average age of debtors, the average age of creditors and the average age of finished stock while maintaining its existing sales volume.

(c) Using the data in task 2.1 and your solution to task 2.2(a), address the issues raised by Angela Newton.

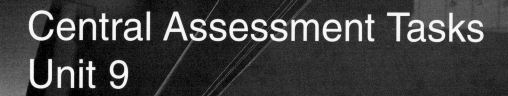

Central Assessment Tasks Unit 9

Alton Products plc & Wynn plc

recommended timing 3 hours plus 15 minutes reading time

SECTION 1: ALTON PRODUCTS PLC

DATA

You are employed as a management accountant in the head office of Alton Products plc. One of your tasks involves helping to prepare quarterly budgets for the divisional companies of Alton Products. Each quarter consists of 12 five-day weeks for both production and sales purposes.

One division, Safety Care makes two chemicals, *Delta* and *Omega*. These are sold in standard boxes. Both products use the same material and labour but in different proportions. You have been provided with the following information relating to the two products for quarter 3, the 12 weeks ending 29 September 20-3.

	Delta	*Omega*
• Budgeted sales		
Quarter 3: 12 weeks to 29 September 20-3	3,000 boxes	2,400 boxes
Quarter 4: 12 weeks to 22 December 20-3	3,300 boxes	2,640 boxes

	Delta	*Omega*
• Finished stocks for quarter 3		
Opening stock	630 boxes	502 boxes
Closing stock (days sales in quarter 4)	6 days	8 days

	Delta	*Omega*
• Production inputs		
Material per box	12 kilograms	15 kilograms
Labour per box	3 hours	6 hours

• Material stocks and costs for quarter 3	
Opening stock (kilograms)	13,560
Closing stock (kilograms)	21,340
Budgeted purchase price per kilogram	£7.00

• Labour costs for quarter 3

52 production employees work a 36-hour week and are each paid £180 per week. Any overtime is payable at £7.50 per hour.

• Faulty production

10% of production is found to be faulty on completion. Faulty production has to be scrapped and has no scrap value.

Task 1.1   The production director of Safety Care asks you to prepare the following data for quarter 3:

(a)   the number of boxes of *Delta* and *Omega* planned to be in closing stock

(b)   the number of labour hours available for production before incurring overtime

(c)   the production budget for *Delta* and *Omega* required to meet the budgeted sales

(d)   the material purchases budget in kilograms and cost

(e)   the labour budget in hours and cost.

DATA

Home Care is another division of Alton Products plc. In January 20-4, the sales director of Home Care, Sue Keane, provides you with the following sales volume data for one of Home Care's products. This was a new product in January 20-1 and it was expected that sales would show seasonal fluctuations.

UNITS SOLD BY QUARTER (in thousands)

Year	Quarter 1	Quarter 2	Quarter 3	Quarter 4
20-1	18	32	30	24
20-2	26	46	44	34
20-3	36	62	56	42

Sue Keane asks you to analyse the sales volume data for this product in order to identify the trend and seasonal variations.

Task 1.2   Prepare notes for Sue Keane in which you carry out the analysis as follows:

(a)   Calculate the *Centred Four-point Moving Average Trend* figures for the given data, working to one decimal place.

(b)   Calculate the seasonal variations on the assumption that they are proportional (percentage) seasonal variations, working to the nearest 1%.

(c)   Use your results in (a) and (b) to forecast the sales volume for quarter 1 and quarter 2 of year 20-4, giving your answers to the nearest thousand units.

(d)   Suggest **one** way in which your analysis of the sales volume data and the forecasts may be used by Home Care to assist with the planning and allocation of resources.

(e)   State **one** reservation you may have about the use of your analysis of the data for the purposes of forecasting future sales volumes of the product.

SECTION 2: WYNN PLC

DATA

Wynn plc produces a specialised fuel product, NY, which cannot be kept as work-in-progress and when completed is stored in sealed drums. You are employed as an assistant to the management accountant of Wynn plc.

For the year ended 31 October 20-1, the budget was for 100,000 drums of NY to be produced and sold, but the actual production was 108,000 drums and sales for the period amounted to 102,000 drums. An operating results statement, showing the budgeted and actual results and other information, is shown below.

Wynn plc Operating results for the year ended 31 October 20-1

	Budget		Actual	
Sales Volume (drums of NY)		100,000		102,000
Production Volume (drums of NY)		100,000		108,000
	£000s	£000s	£000s	£000s
Turnover		3,600		3,876
Direct costs:				
Material	640		714	
Production labour	760		782	
Power	172		170	
Direct Cost of Sales		1,572		1,666
		2,028		2,210
Fixed Overheads		1,240		1,200
Operating profit		788		1,010

Notes

1   There are no opening or closing work-in-progress or opening stock of finished goods.

2   The closing stock of finished goods of 6,000 drums is valued for the purposes of the above statement at average actual direct production cost per drum. The direct production cost of 108,000 drums is therefore split between the value of the closing stock and the cost of sales as shown in the following table:

	Closing Stock	Cost of Sales	Production Cost
Number of drums	6,000	102,000	108,000
	£000s	£000s	£000s
Material	42	714	756
Production labour	46	782	828
Power	10	170	180
Total direct cost	98	1,666	1,764

3   The cost of direct material is a variable cost.

4   The cost of direct production labour is a fixed cost, because the employees are paid a fixed wage. The employees available are sufficient to produce up to 120,000 drums of NY.

5   The cost of power is semi-variable and the fixed part of the cost allowed for in the budget is £40,000. However, the fixed part of the actual cost is £36,360, due to re-negotiation of the contract with the power company.

Task 2.1

(a)   Calculate the following:

(i)   the budgeted unit selling price

(ii)   the budgeted material cost per drum of NY

(iii)   the budgeted marginal cost (variable cost) of power

(iv)   the actual unit selling price

(v)   the actual material cost per drum of NY

(vi)   the actual marginal cost of power, using the *production cost* given in Note 2 and the actual fixed cost of power given in Note 5

(b)   Prepare a *marginal costing operating results statement*, comparing the actual results with a flexible budget for production of 108,000 drums and sales of 102,000 drums and showing the variances.

DATA

On reviewing the marginal costing statement you have prepared, the Production Manager of Wynn plc asks you the following questions:

(a)   What is the advantage of preparing another budget to compare with the actual results?

(b)   Why does your statement show a different profit figure for the actual results?

(c)   Is it necessary to investigate the reasons for all the variances? If not, do I just investigate adverse variances?

Task   2.2

Write a Memo in reply to the Production Manager, giving brief explanations in answer to the three questions (a), (b) and (c) above.

Central Assessment Tasks
Unit 9

Aspen Ltd & Rivermede Ltd

recommended timing 3 hours plus 15 minutes reading time

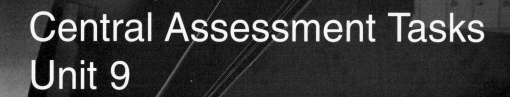

SECTION 1: ASPEN LTD

DATA

You are a management accountant employed by Aspen Ltd and you report to Adrian Jones, the managing director. One of your responsibilities is the production of budgets. Aspen Ltd only has one customer, Advanced Industries plc, for whom it makes the Zeta, a specialist product. Advanced Industries demands that Aspen keeps a minimum closing stock of Zetas in case there is an error in the forecast requirements. There is no work-in-progress at any time.

- Both companies divide the year into four-week periods. Each week consists of five days and each day comprises eight hours.

- Advanced Industries plc has recently informed Aspen Ltd of its Zeta requirements for the five periods ending Friday 25 May 20-1. The details are produced below.

Forecast demand for Zetas

Four weeks ending:	2 February	2 March	30 March	27 April	25 May
	Period 1	Period 2	Period 3	Period 4	Period 5
Number of Zetas required	5,700	5,700	6,840	6,460	6,080

Closing stocks of Zetas

Closing stocks are to equal 3 days of the next period's demand for Zetas.

The production director gives you the following information:

- The actual opening stocks for period 1, the four weeks ending 2 February, will be 1,330 Zetas.

- Each Zeta requires 6 litres of material.

- The material is currently supplied under a long-term contract at a cost of £8.00 per litre and is made exclusively for Aspen by Contrax plc.

- Contrax only has sufficient production capacity to make a maximum of 34,000 litres in any four-week period. Aspen normally purchases the material in the same four-week period it is used.

- Should Aspen require more than 34,000 litres in a four-week period, Contrax would be willing to supply additional material in the preceding period, providing it had spare capacity.

- There is a readily available alternative source for the material but the cost is £12.00 per litre.

- Before buying from the alternative source, any shortage of material in a period should be overcome, where possible, by first purchasing extra material from Contrax in the **immediately preceding** period.

- There are 78 production employees who are paid a guaranteed basic wage of £160 per 40-hour week.

- Each Zeta should take 2 labour hours to make but, due to temporary technical difficulties, the workforce is only able to operate at 95 per cent efficiency in periods 1 to 4.

- Any overtime incurred is payable at a rate of £6.00 per hour.

Task 1.1

Adrian Jones asks you to prepare the following budgets for each of the periods 1 to 4:

(a)   the production budget in Zetas, using the stock levels given in the data

(b)   the material purchases budget in litres

(c)   the cost of the material purchases

(d)   the labour budget in hours, including any overtime hours

(e)   the cost of the labour budget, including the cost of any overtime

DATA

On receiving your budgets, Adrian Jones, the managing director, tells you that:

• he is concerned about the cost of the planned overtime and the extra cost of purchasing materials from the alternative supplier

• the minimum demand in any four-week period is forecast to be 5,700 Zetas

• it is not possible to reduce costs by Advanced Industries plc improving its current method of forecasting

However, he believes that some immediate and longer-term cost savings are possible.

Task 1.2

Write a Memo to Adrian Jones. In your Memo, you should:

(a)   use the budget information prepared in Task 1.1 to identify **one** immediate possible cost saving proposal other than renegotiating the conditions imposed by Advanced Industries plc

(b)   calculate the value of the cost savings in the proposal identified in part a)

(c)   use the forecast minimum demand for Zetas to show whether or not:

    (i)   the need to obtain material supplies from the alternative source is a short-term problem, and

    (ii)   the need for overtime payments is also a short-term problem

(d)   suggest **two** cost savings which may be possible in the longer term.

SECTION 2: RIVERMEDE LTD

DATA

Rivermede Ltd makes a single product called the Fasta. Last year, Steven Jones, the managing director of Rivermede Ltd, attended a course on budgetary control. As a result, he agreed to revise the way budgets were prepared in the company. Rather than imposing targets for managers, he encouraged participation by senior managers in the preparation of budgets.

An initial budget was prepared but Mike Fisher, the sales director, considered that the budgeted sales volume was set too high. He explained that setting too high a budgeted sales volume would mean his sales staff would be demotivated because they would not be able to achieve that sales volume. Steven Jones agreed to use the revised sales volume suggested by Mike Fisher.

Both the initial and revised budgets are reproduced below, complete with the actual results for the year ended 31 May 20-9.

Rivermede Ltd – budgeted and actual costs for the year ended 31 May 20-9				
	Original Budget	Revised Budget	Actual Results	Variances from revised Budget
Fasta production & sales (units)	24,000	20,000	22,000	2,000 F
	£	£	£	£
Variable costs				
Material	216,000	180,000	206,800	26,800 A
Labour	288,000	240,000	255,200	15,200 A
Semi-variable costs				
Heat, light and Power	31,000	27,000	33,400	6,400 A
Fixed costs				
Rent, rates & depreciation	40,000	40,000	38,000	2,000 F
	575,000	487,000	533,400	46,400 A

Assumptions in the two budgets

1   No change in input prices.

2   No change in the quantity of variable inputs per Fasta.

As the management accountant at Rivermede Ltd, one of your tasks is to check that invoices have been properly coded. On checking the actual invoices for heat, light and power for the year to 31 May 20-9, you find that one invoice for £7,520 had been incorrectly coded. The invoice should have been coded to materials.

Task 2.1

(a)   Using the information in the original and revised budgets, identify:
- the variable cost of material and labour per Fasta
- the fixed and unit variable cost within heat, light and power

(b)   Prepare a flexible budget performance statement, including variances, for Rivermede Ltd after correcting for the miscoding of the invoice.

DATA

On reviewing the flexible budget performance report you have prepared in Task 2.1:
- Mike Fisher, the sales director states that it shows that his participation in revising the sales budget motivated the sales staff to achieve better results.
- Steven Jones, the managing director, is not sure whether the participative approach has been successful, in particular because the effects of the revised budget were not fully investigated before it was implemented. He considers that the use of flexible budgeting and the reporting of results should enable him to improve the planning process as well as the control of the business.

Task 2.2

(a)   Give **two** reasons why the actual sales may have exceeded the revised budget, other than the reason given by Mike Fisher.

(b)   Explain briefly how flexible budgeting and the reporting of results can assist with planning and control through the use of 'feedforward' and 'feedback' of information.

Central Assessment Tasks Unit 9

Ryedell Ltd and Colour plc

recommended timing 3 hours plus 15 minutes reading time

SECTION 1: RYEDELL LTD

Data

Ryedell Ltd is a manufacturer of two products, the Rye and the Dell.

You are employed as an assistant management accountant in Ryedell Ltd, particularly involved in preparing budgets.

Both products Rye and Dell are made using the same direct material and labour, but in different amounts.

Budgets are prepared for periods of 8 weeks, each week being 5 working days.

The underlying trend over the last 3 years in sales demand for each of the two products has remained steady (neither increasing nor decreasing), but there are seasonal variations in demand. These have been calculated as percentages of the average for the six 8-week budget periods in the year. (Production ceases at the end of November for four weeks, for essential maintenance work and holidays).

For the next 8-week budget period, ending 30 November 20-1, which is period 6 of the year, the following information is available for preparation of the budget.

Product	Rye	Dell
Average (trend) sales units	1,000	2,000
Period 6 seasonal variation in demand	+30%	+20%
Direct material in each completed unit	3 kg	1 kg
Direct labour hours per unit	1.5 hours	0.9 hours

The budgeted direct labour rate is £5.60 per hour and the basic working week is 40 hours for full-time employees. Any additional hours are paid at an overtime rate of time and a half, i.e. £8.40 per hour. There are 12.5 full-time equivalent employees working on production. For the next period, the target efficiency ratio for direct labour is 90%.

The budgeted opening and closing stock levels for the next 12-week period are as follows:

	Opening stock	Closing stock
Direct Material	900 kg	1,100 kg
Product Rye completed units	350 units	250 units
Product Dell completed units	420 units	400 units
(There are no stocks of work in progress).		

The budgeted cost of direct material is £5.50 per kg. The manufacturing process for both the Rye and the Dell is such that 8% of the material input to the production process is unavoidably lost and this must be allowed for in calculating the material usage budget.

Task 1.1

For Ryedell Ltd for the 8-week period ending 30 November 20-1, calculate the following:

(a)   the sales budget in units of each of the two products Rye and Dell

(b)   the production budget in units of each of the two products Rye and Dell

(c)   the total direct material usage budget in kg

(d)   the total direct material purchases budget in kg and in £

(e) the standard direct labour hours required for production

(f) the total hours to be budgeted for production workers

(g) the total budgeted cost of production labour including overtime premium.

DATA

Don Leeds has recently been appointed as the financial director of Ryedell Ltd. On reviewing the budget you have prepared, he makes the following comments:

• I am concerned that it seems necessary to ask production staff to do overtime and also that this increases the cost of production. I notice the budget is based on only 90% efficiency.

• I am considering whether we should employ more production staff or concentrate on improving efficiency, perhaps through a bonus scheme or permanent wage increase.

Task 1.2

Write a Memo to Don Leeds. Referring to the data given for Task 1.1 and the budgets prepared for the given period where relevant, your memo should:

(a) state and explain briefly **one** advantage and **one** disadvantage to Ryedell Ltd of:

(i) using overtime when required for production

(ii) employing more production staff

(iii) introducing a bonus scheme to improve efficiency

(iv) giving production staff a permanent wage increase to motivate them to improve efficiency.

(b) suggest one way, other than those in part (a) above, in which Ryedell Ltd may be able to reduce or eliminate the necessity for overtime.

SECTION 2: COLOUR PLC – RED LTD

DATA

Colour plc has two subsidiaries, Red Ltd and Green Ltd. Red Ltd makes only one product, a part only used by Green Ltd. Because Green is the only customer and there is no market price for the part, the part is sold to Green at cost.

Last year, Red prepared two provisional budgets because Green was not certain how many parts it would buy from Red in the current year. These two budgets are reproduced below.

Red Ltd provisional budgets 12 months to 30 November 20-8		
Volume (units)	18,000	20,000
	£	£
Material	180,000	200,000
Labour	308,000	340,000
Power and Maintenance	33,000	35,000
Rent, insurance and depreciation	98,000	98,000
Total cost	619,000	673,000

Shortly afterwards, Green told Red that it needed 20,000 parts over the year to 30 November 20-8. Red's budget for the year was then based on that level of production.

During the financial year, Green Ltd only bought 19,500 parts. Red's performance statement for the year to 30 November 20-8 is reproduced below.

Red Ltd performance statement – year to 30 November 20-8			
	Budget	Actual	Variance
Volume (units)	20,000	19,500	
	£	£	£
Material	200,000	197,000	3,000 F
Labour	340,000	331,000	9,000 F
Power and Maintenance	35,000	35,000	–
Rent, insurance and depreciation	98,000	97,500	500 F
Total cost	673,000	660,500	12,500 F
F = Favourable, A = Adverse			

Task 2.1

(a) Using the data in the provisional budgets, calculate the fixed and variable cost elements within each of the expenditure headings.

(b) Using the data in the performance statement and your solution to part a), prepare a revised performance statement using flexible budgeting. Your statement should show both the revised budget and the variances.

DATA

On receiving the flexible budget statement you have prepared, the Managing Director of Red Ltd comments as follows:

As Red Ltd is a cost centre and is dependent on Green Ltd for demand for our product, we prepared two cost budgets originally. The flexible budget you prepared is more useful for comparison with the actual results, but I think it could be improved further to speed up control action. It should also be possible to set up a spreadsheet to prepare budgets for different levels of production more quickly.

Task 2.2

(a) Explain what is meant by the term 'cost centre'.

(b) Suggest **two** types of 'control action' which the managing director may take as a result of comparing the actual results with the flexible budget.

(c) Suggest **one** way in which the reporting of results could be improved to speed up control action.

(d) Explain briefly, referring to the methods you have used in Task 2.1 to illustrate your answer, the data which would be required as input in order to use a spreadsheet for the preparation of budgets for different levels of production. State in words a general formula for the total of a semi-variable cost, on which the spreadsheet formulae for the calculation of costs in the flexible budget would be based.

Central Assessment Tasks Unit 9

Star Fuels and Professor Heath

reproduced by kind permission of AAT

recommended timing 2 hours plus 15 minutes reading time

NOTE TO STUDENTS

This assessment has been issued by AAT to provide guidance for students completing Central Assessments.

The Assessment is divided into two sections.

The recommended timing is as follows:

Section 1	50 minutes
Section 2	70 minutes

Note: subsequent AAT Central Assessments have allowed 3 hours plus 15 minutes reading time.

SECTION 1: STAR FUELS

(Suggested time allocation: 50 minutes)

DATA

Star Fuels is a multinational oil company selling oil for industrial and domestic purposes through a network of distributors. Distributors purchase fuel oil from Star Fuels and then sell it on to their own customers.

A regular complaint of the distributors is that they either have to pay for the fuel on delivery to their storage tanks or be charged interest on a daily basis on the amount owed. This problem could be reduced if the distributors were able to forecast their demands more accurately.

You are employed as the Assistant Management Accountant to Northern Fuel Distributors Ltd, a major distributor of Star Fuel's fuel oils. You recently attended a meeting with Mary Lamberton, a member of Star Fuel's central staff. At the meeting, she demonstrated a statistical software package used for estimating the demand for fuel oil. The user enters sales volumes per period and the package then calculates the least-squares regression equation for the data. This is in the form of $y = a + bx$ where x is the time period, y is the forecast and a and b are terms derived from the original data. Following further inputs by the user, the package can also estimate seasonal variations. Two forms of seasonal variation are calculated: the first calculates the seasonal variance as an absolute amount, the second as a percentage.

One week after the meeting, your copy of the software arrives at the head office of Northern Fuel Distributors Ltd and you immediately set about testing its capability. Purely for the purpose of testing, you assume seasonal variations occur quarterly. You enter this assumption along with the sales turnover figures for fuel oil for the last 20 quarters. Within moments, the software outputs the following information.

Regression line:

$$y = £2,000,000 + £40,000x$$

Seasonal variations

Quarter	A	B	C	D
Amount	+£350,000	+£250,000	−£400,000	−£200,000
Percentage	+15%	+10%	−15%	−10%

Quarter A refers to the first quarter of annual data, B to the second quarter, C to the third and D to the fourth. The pattern then repeats itself. In terms of the specific data you input, seasonal variation A refers to quarter 17, B to quarter 18, C to quarter 19 and D to quarter 20.

Actual sales turnover for quarters 17 to 20 was as follows:

Quarter	17	18	19	20
Sales turnover	£3,079,500	£3,002,400	£2,346,500	£2,490,200

Task 1.1

Making use of the formula derived by the software package, calculate the forecast sales turnover for quarters 17 to 20 using:

(a)   the absolute seasonal variations

(b)   the percentage seasonal variations

Task 1.2

(a)   From your answers to Task 1.1, determine which method of calculating seasonal variations gives the best estimate of actual sales turnover.

(b)   Having identified the preferred method, use that method to forecast the sales turnover for quarters 21 to 24.

Task 1.3

Write a memorandum to your Managing Director. The memorandum should:

(a)   explain what is meant by seasonal variations and seasonally adjusted data; illustrate your explanation with examples relevant to Northern Fuel Distributors Ltd

(b)   suggest why your chosen method of seasonal adjustment might be more accurate

(c)   show how an understanding of seasonal variations and seasonally adjusted data can help Northern Fuel Distributors Ltd to be more efficient

(d)   identify **two** weaknesses within your approach to forecasting undertaken in Tasks 1.1 and 1.2

SECTION 2: PROFESSOR HEATH

(Suggested time allocation: 70 minutes)

DATA

It is 1 March and Professor Pauline Heath has just taken up her new appointment as the Head of the Postgraduate Business Studies Department in a new university. Due to unfilled vacancies throughout the current academic year, the department has had to rely on part-time academic staff. The cost of part-time staff who are self-employed is coded to account number 321, while those who are taxed under the Pay-As-You-Earn system are charged to account code 002. Both types of staff enter their claims within ten days of each month-end and these then appear in the management reports of the subsequent month. There are also unfilled clerical and administrative staff vacancies.

The university has a residential conference centre, which the department makes use of from time to time. Sometimes this is because the department's allocated rooms are all in use and sometimes because the department teaches at weekends. The charge for the use of the centre is coded to account 673. An alternative to using the conference centre is to hire outside facilities at local hotels, in which case the expenditure is coded to account 341.

The main forms of income are tuition fees and a higher education grant from the government. The extent of this grant is known before the commencement of the academic year and is payable in two parts, one-third at the end of December and the balance at the end of April.

One of Professor Heath's first tasks was to check the enrolments for the current year. The financial and academic year commenced on 1 September and is subdivided into three terms, each lasting four months. The Autumn term commenced on 1 September and the Spring term on 1 January. All courses commence at the beginning of the Autumn term, the MBA and MSc courses lasting three terms and the diploma course two terms.

The departmental administrator has presented Professor Heath with the enrolment data for the current academic year. Whilst absorbing this information, she has also received the latest management accounts for the department. Both sets of information are reproduced below.

Professor Heath is experiencing difficulties in understanding the latest management report. She has written a memo to the university's finance director expressing her anxieties about the presentation of the report and its detailed contents.

Enrolment data-current academic year	Fee (£)	Enrolments	Income (£)
MBA – three terms	3,500	160	560,000
MSc – three terms	3,200	80	256,000
Diploma Course – two terms	1,200	100	120,000
			936,000

Department of Postgraduate Business Studies

Monthly Management Report – February

Code	Account heading	Annual budget	6 months to 28 February			Budget remaining
			Actual	Budget	Variance	
	Expenses					
001	Full-time academic	600,000	230,000	300,000	70,000	370,000
002	Part-time academic	84,000	48,000	42,000	–6,000	36,000
003	Clerical and administration	84,000	36,000	42,000	6,000	48,000
218	Teaching and learning material	30,000	0	15,000	15,000	30,000
321	Teaching and research fees	20,000	19,000	10,000	–9,000	1,000
331	Agency staff (clerical and administrative)	300	2,400	150	–2,250	–2,100
341	External room hire	1,000	400	500	100	600
434	Course advertising (press)	26,000	600	13,000	12,400	25,400
455	Postage and telephone recharge	8,000	1,200	4,000	2,800	6,800
673	Internal room hire	24,000	14,000	12,000	–2,000	10,000
679	Central services recharge	340,000	170,000	170,000	0	170,000
680	Rental light and heat recharge	260,000	130,000	130,000	0	130,000
		1,477,300	651,600	738,650	87,050	825,700
	Income					
802	Tuition fees	900,000	936,000	900,000	–36,000	–36,000
890	Higher education grant	750,000	250,000	250,000	0	500,000
		1,650,000	1,186,000	1,150,000	–36,000	464,000
	Net surplus/deficit	172,700	534,400	411,350	–123,050	–361,700

Task 2.1

(a) Rearrange the account headings into a more meaningful form for managers. This should include columnar headings for any financial data you feel is appropriate but you do not need to include any figures.

(b) Briefly justify your proposals.

Task 2.2

In her memo, Professor Heath states that the current form of report does not help her manage her department. Identify the strengths and weaknesses apparent in the current system, other than the presentational ones covered in task 2.1, and make and justify outline proposals that will help her manage the department.

Task 2.3

Referring to the detailed financial data under the heading of Income, reproduce the actual income to date in a form consistent with accounting principles.